Entertainment Directory

# DUBLIN
## TRAVEL GUIDE

**SHOPS, RESTAURANTS, ATTRACTIONS & NIGHTLIFE**

The Most Positively
Reviewed and Recommended
by Locals and Travelers

# DUBLIN

## TRAVEL GUIDE

**SHOPS, RESTAURANTS, ATTRACTIONS & NIGHTLIFE**

DUBLIN TRAVEL GUIDE 2022
Shops, Restaurants, Arts, Entertainment & Nightlife

© Ronald B. Kinnoch
© E.G.P. Editorial

ISBN-13: 9798748183345

# INDEX

## DUBLIN TRAVEL GUIDE

### Shops, Restaurants, Arts, Entertainment & Nightlife

*This directory is dedicated to Dublin Business Owners and Managers who provide the experience that the locals and tourists enjoy. Thanks you very much for all that you do and thank for being the "People Choice".*

*Thanks to everyone that posts their reviews online and the amazing reviews sites that make our life easier.*

*The places listed in this book are the most positively reviewed and recommended by locals and travelers from around the world.*

*Thank you for your time and enjoy the directory that is designed with locals and tourist in mind!*

# TOP 500 SHOPS

The Most Recommended by Locals & Trevelers

(From #1 to #500)

#1
**Hodges Figgis**
**Category:** Bookstore
**Average price:** Modest
**Area:** South Inner City
**Address:** 56-58 Dawson St Dublin 2
**Phone:** 353 1 6774754

#2
**Om Diva**
**Category:** Women's Clothing,
Vintage, Consignment
**Average price:** Modest
**Area:** South Inner City
**Address:** 27 Drury St Dublin 2
**Phone:** 353 1 6791211

#3
**Avoca**
**Category:** Women's Clothing, Cafe
**Average price:** Modest
**Area:** South Inner City
**Address:** 11-13 Suffolk St Dublin 2
**Phone:** 353 1 6774215

#4
**George's St Arcade**
**Category:** Shopping Center,
Coffee & Tea
**Average price:** Modest
**Area:** South Inner City
**Address:** S Great George's St Dublin 2
**Phone:** 353 1 6715917

#5
**Chapters Bookstore**
**Category:** Bookstore
**Average price:** Inexpensive
**Area:** Parnell Square
**Address:** Parnell St Dublin 1
**Phone:** 353 1 8723297

#6
**The Pen Corner**
**Category:** Cards & Stationery
**Average price:** Expensive
**Area:** South Inner City
**Address:** 12 College Green Dublin 2
**Phone:** 353 1 6793641

#7
**Marks & Spencer**
**Category:** Women's Clothing,
Men's Clothing
**Average price:** Modest
**Area:** South Inner City
**Address:** 15-20 Grafton St Dublin 2
**Phone:** 353 1 6797855

#8
**Lucy's Lounge**
**Category:** Vintage, Consignment
**Average price:** Inexpensive
**Area:** South Inner City
**Address:** 11 Fownes St Dublin 2
**Phone:** 353 1 6774779

#9
**Jervis Shopping Centre**
**Category:** Shopping Center
**Average price:** Modest
**Area:** North Inner City
**Address:** 125 Upper Abbey St Dublin 1
**Phone:** 353 1 8781323

#10
**Dundrum Town Centre**
**Category:** Shopping Center
**Average price:** Expensive
**Area:** Dundrum
**Address:** Sandyford Rd Dublin 16
**Phone:** 353 1 2991700

#11
**This Is Knit**
**Category:** Arts & Crafts
**Average price:** Modest
**Area:** South Inner City
**Address:** 59 South William St Dublin 2
**Phone:** 353 1 6709981

#12
**Secret Book & Record Store**
**Category:** Bookstore, Vinyl Records
**Average price:** Inexpensive
**Area:** South Inner City
**Address:** 15A Wicklow St
Dublin 2
**Phone:** 353 1 6797272

#13
**Stephen's Green
Shopping Centre**
**Category:** Shopping Center
**Average price:** Modest
**Area:** South Inner City
**Address:** Stephens Green West Dublin 2
**Phone:** 353 1 4780888

#14
**River Island**
**Category:** Accessories, Men's Clothing
**Average price:** Expensive
**Area:** South Inner City
**Address:** 12 Henry St Dublin
**Phone:** 353 818 333073

#15
**Siopaella**
**Category:** Vintage, Consignment, Women's
Clothing, Men's Clothing
**Average price:** Modest
**Area:** Temple Bar
**Address:** 8a Crow St Dublin 2
**Phone:** 353 1 6779106

#16
**Forbidden Planet**
**Category:** Comic Books, Hobby Shop
**Average price:** Modest
**Area:** Temple Bar
**Address:** 5-6 Crampton Quay Dublin 2
**Phone:** 353 1 6710688

#17
**Liffey Valley Shoping Centre**
**Category:** Shopping Center
**Average price:** Modest
**Area:** Palmerstown
**Address:** Font Hill Rd Dublin
**Phone:** 353 1 6233300

#18
**IKEA**
**Category:** Furniture Store, Home Decor
**Average price:** Inexpensive
**Area:** St. Margaret's
**Address:** 11 Saint Margaret's Rd Dublin
**Phone:** 44 1890 987938

#19
**Avoca**
**Category:** Irish, Home Decor,
Department Store
**Average price:** Modest
**Area:** Rathcoole
**Address:** N7 Naas Rd Dublin
**Phone:** 353 1 2571810

#20
**The Gutter Bookshop**
**Category:** Bookstore
**Average price:** Modest
**Area:** Temple Bar
**Address:** Cow's Lane Dublin 8
**Phone:** 353 1 6799206

#21
**Schuh**
**Category:** Shoe Store
**Average price:** Modest
**Area:** South Inner City
**Address:** Unit 5 Dublin 1
**Phone:** 353 1 8730433

#22
**Topshop**
**Category:** Women's Clothing,
Outlet Store
**Average price:** Expensive
**Area:** South Inner City
**Address:** Stephen's Green
Dublin 2
**Phone:** 353 1 6334803

#23
**Rua Dublin**
**Category:** Home Decor,
Accessories, Concept Shop
**Average price:** Modest
**Area:** North Inner City
**Address:** 55 Capel St Dublin 1
**Phone:** 353 1 8748051

#24
**Penneys**
**Category:** Women's Clothing,
Men's Clothing, Children's Clothing
**Average price:** Inexpensive
**Area:** North Inner City
**Address:** 47 Mary St Dublin 1
**Phone:** 353 1 8727788

#25
**O'Connell St**
**Category:** Department Store
**Average price:** Modest
**Area:** North Inner City
**Address:** O'Connell St Dublin 1
**Phone:** 353 86 2356016

#26
**Brown Thomas**
**Category:** Department Store
**Average price:** Exclusive
**Area:** South Inner City
**Address:** 88-95 Grafton St Dublin 2
**Phone:** 353 1 6795666

#27
**Evans Art Supplies**
**Category:** Art Supplies
**Average price:** Modest
**Area:** North Inner City
**Address:** 5/6 Meeting House Lane Dublin 7
**Phone:** 353 1 8726855

#28
**Temple Bar Book Market**
**Category:** Books, Mags, Music & Video
**Average price:** Inexpensive
**Area:** Temple Bar
**Address:** Temple Bar Square Dublin 2
**Phone:** 353 1 6772255

#29
**Cows Lane Designer Studio**
**Category:** Arts & Crafts
**Average price:** Modest
**Area:** Temple Bar
**Address:** 2 Pudding Row Dublin 8
**Phone:** 353 1 5240001

#30
**Retro**
**Category:** Women's Clothing
**Average price:** Modest
**Area:** South Inner City
**Address:** 22 S Great Georges St Dublin 2
**Phone:** 353 1 6337891

#31
**Dunnes**
**Category:** Grocery, Department Store,
Kitchen & Bath
**Average price:** Modest
**Area:** South Inner City
**Address:** Stephen's Green
Shopping Ctr Dublin 2
**Phone:** 353 1 4780188

#33
**Jenny Vander**
**Category:** Vintage, Consignment
**Average price:** Expensive
**Area:** South Inner City
**Address:** 50 Drury St
Dublin 2
**Phone:** 353 1 6770406

#32
**Penneys**
**Category:** Department Store
**Average price:** Inexpensive
**Area:** South Inner City
**Address:** O'Connell St 1 Dublin 1
**Phone:** 353 1 8720466

#34
**Sub-City**
**Category:** Comic Books, Bookstore
**Average price:** Modest
**Area:** South Inner City
**Address:** 62 Dame St Dublin 2
**Phone:** 353 1 6771902

#35
**TK Maxx**
**Category:** Women's Clothing,
Men's Clothing, Outlet Store
**Average price:** Modest
**Area:** South Inner City
**Address:** Saint Stephens Green
Shopping Center Dublin 2
**Phone:** 353 1 4757080

#36
**Lush**
**Category:** Cosmetics & Beauty
**Average price:** Modest
**Area:** South Inner City
**Address:** 116 Grafton St Dublin 2
**Phone:** 353 1 6770392

#37
**Project Arts Centre**
**Category:** Performing Arts, Art Gallery
**Average price:** Modest
**Area:** Temple Bar
**Address:** 39 East Essex St Dublin 2
**Phone:** 353 1 6712321

#38
**Kilkenny**
**Category:** Kitchen & Bath,
Arts & Crafts, Accessories
**Average price:** Expensive
**Area:** South Inner City
**Address:** 5-6 Nassau St Dublin 2
**Phone:** 353 1 6777066

#39
**Hugh Lane Municipal
Gallery of Modern Art**
**Category:** Museum, Art Gallery
**Average price:** Inexpensive
**Area:** Rotunda, Parnell Square
**Address:** Parnell Square Dublin 1
**Phone:** 353 1 8741903

#40
**Schuh**
**Category:** Shoe Store
**Average price:** Modest
**Area:** North Inner City
**Address:** 47-48 O'Connell St Dublin 1
**Phone:** 353 1 8723234

#41
**Harlequin**
**Category:** Vintage,
Consignment, Jewelry
**Average price:** Modest
**Area:** South Inner City
**Address:** 13 Castle Market Dublin 2
**Phone:** 353 1 6710202

#42
**Bow and Pearl**
**Category:** Women's Clothing
**Average price:** Expensive
**Area:** Rathgar
**Address:** 13 Ranelagh Village Dublin 6
**Phone:** 353 1 4967408

#43
**Lush**
**Category:** Cosmetics & Beauty
**Average price:** Modest
**Area:** North Inner City
**Address:** 33 Henry St Dublin 1
**Phone:** 353 1 8735735

#44
**Rhinestones**
**Category:** Jewelry, Antiques
**Average price:** Expensive
**Area:** South Inner City
**Address:** 18 Saint Andrew's St Dublin 2
**Phone:** 353 1 6790759

#45
**Budda Bag**
**Category:** Furniture Store
**Average price:** Exclusive
**Area:** North Inner City
**Address:** 1 Jervis House Dublin 1
**Phone:** 353 1 8734245

#46
**Camden Clothing**
**Category:** Sports Wear
**Average price:** Modest
**Area:** Harcourt
**Address:** 29 Camden St Dublin 2
**Phone:** 353 1 4175961

#47
**Tamp & Stitch**
**Category:** Jewelry, Coffee & Tea
**Average price:** Modest
**Area:** Temple Bar
**Address:** Unit 3 Scarlet Row Dublin 8
**Phone:** 353 1 5154705

#48
**Eason**
**Category:** Bookstore, Cards & Stationery
**Average price:** Modest
**Area:** North Inner City
**Address:** 40 Lower O'connell St Dublin 1
**Phone:** 353 1 8733811

#49
**Nimble Fingers**
**Category:** Art Supplies
**Average price:** Modest
**Area:** Stillorgan
**Address:** Old Dublin Rd Dublin
**Phone:** 353 1 2880788

#50
**Grahams Shoes**
**Category:** Shoe Store
**Average price:** Modest
**Area:** South Inner City
**Address:** 22/26 Exchequer St Dublin 2
**Phone:** 353 1 6774645

#51
**Donnelly Leathers**
**Category:** Leather Goods, Luggage
**Average price:** Modest
**Area:** South Inner City
**Address:** 11 Harcourt St Dublin 2
**Phone:** 353 1 4758811

#52
**Dunnes Hardware**
**Category:** Hardware Store
**Average price:** Modest
**Area:** South Inner City
**Address:** 27 Wexford St Dublin 2
**Phone:** 353 1 4780809

#53
**Arnotts, PLC**
**Category:** Department Store
**Average price:** Modest
**Area:** North Inner City
**Address:** 12 Henry St Dublin 1
**Phone:** 353 1 8050400

#54
**Dublin Camera Exchange**
**Category:** Photography Store
**Average price:** Expensive
**Area:** Dún Laoghaire
**Address:** 63 Georges St Dublin 2
**Phone:** 353 1 4784125

#55
**Kitchen Complements**
**Category:** Kitchen & Bath
**Average price:** Expensive
**Area:** South Inner City
**Address:** South Anne St Dublin 2
**Phone:** 353 1 6770734

#56
**Carroll's Irish Gifts**
**Category:** Gift Shop
**Average price:** Modest
**Area:** Temple Bar
**Address:** 44 Henry St Dublin 1
**Phone:** 353 1 8721215

#57
**Lenehans Hardware**
**Category:** Hardware Store, Home Decor
**Average price:** Modest
**Area:** Rathmines
**Address:** 7-9 Rathgar Rd Dublin 6
**Phone:** 353 1 4979791

#58
**Rothar**
**Category:** Community Service, Bikes
**Average price:** Inexpensive
**Area:** BRdstone
**Address:** 171 Phibsborough Rd Dublin 7
**Phone:** 353 86 8956157

#59
**Cycle SuperStore**
**Category:** Sports Wear, Bikes
**Average price:** Expensive
**Area:** Tymon
**Address:** 13 Hibernian Industrial
Estate Dublin 3
**Phone:** 353 1 4632270

#60
**The Dolls Store**
**Category:** Toy Store
**Average price:** Expensive
**Area:** South Inner City
**Address:** 59 South William St Dublin 2
**Phone:** 353 1 6753878

#61
**The Winding Stair Bookshop**
**Category:** Bookstore, Restaurant
**Average price:** Expensive
**Area:** North Inner City
**Address:** 40 Ormond Quay Dublin 1
**Phone:** 353 1 8726576

#62
**Laser Specialists**
**Category:** Videos, Video Game Rental
**Average price:** Inexpensive
**Area:** South Inner City
**Address:** 23 South Georges St Dublin 2
**Phone:** 353 1 6711466

#63
**CycleBike**
**Category:** Bike Rentals, Bikes
**Average price:** Expensive
**Area:** North Inner City
**Address:** 4 Saint Marys Abbey Dublin 7
**Phone:** 353 1 8747474

#64
**SkunkFunk**
**Category:** Women's Clothing,
Men's Clothing
**Average price:** Expensive
**Area:** North Inner City
**Address:** Blooms Lane Dublin 1
**Phone:** 353 1 8733561

#65
**James Fox**
**Category:** Tobacco Shop
**Average price:** Expensive
**Area:** South Inner City
**Address:** 119 Grafton St Dublin 2
**Phone:** 353 1 6770533

#66
**Jam Art Factory**
**Category:** Art Gallery, Museum,
Concept Shop
**Average price:** Modest
**Area:** Clanbrassil St
**Address:** 64/65 Patrick St Dublin 8
**Phone:** 353 1 6165671

#67
**National Photographic Archive**
**Category:** Art Gallery
**Average price:** Expensive
**Area:** Temple Bar
**Address:** Meeting House Square Dublin 2
**Phone:** 353 1 6030370

#68
**2-Euro Store**
**Category:** Discount Store
**Average price:** Inexpensive
**Area:** North Inner City
**Address:** Lower Abbey St Dublin 1
**Phone:** 353 1 8745541

#69
**Monsoon**
**Category:** Women's Clothing, Accessories
**Average price:** Expensive
**Area:** South Inner City
**Address:** 64 Grafton St Dublin 2
**Phone:** 353 1 6139059

#70
**Camden Casket**
**Category:** Outlet Store, Grocery
**Average price:** Inexpensive
**Area:** Harcourt
**Address:** 27 Camden St Dublin 2
**Phone:** 353 1 4762075

#71
**Claddagh Records**
**Category:** Music & DVDs
**Average price:** Modest
**Area:** South Inner City
**Address:** 2 Cecilia St
Dublin 2
**Phone:** 353 1 6770262

#72
**Djinn Jewellery**
**Category:** Jewelry
**Average price:** Modest
**Area:** South Inner City
**Address:** 15A Wexford St Dublin 2
**Phone:** 353 1 4759919

#73
**Miss Fantasia's Adult Boutique**
**Category:** Adult
**Average price:** Modest
**Area:** South Inner City
**Address:** 25 William St South Dublin 2
**Phone:** 353 1 6713734

#74
**Dunnes Store**
**Category:** Department Store
**Area:** North Inner City
**Address:** 54/62 Henry St Dublin 1
**Phone:** 353 86 2568507

#75
**Right Click**
**Category:** Computers
**Average price:** Modest
**Area:** Harcourt
**Address:** 70 Camden St Dublin 2
**Phone:** 353 1 4759681

#76
**Perfect Pitch**
**Category:** Musical Instruments
**Average price:** Expensive
**Area:** South Inner City
**Address:** 35 Exchequer St Dublin 2
**Phone:** 353 1 6771553

#77
**L'Occitane**
**Category:** Cosmetics & Beauty
**Average price:** Expensive
**Area:** South Inner City
**Address:** 15 Wicklow St Dublin 2
**Phone:** 353 1 6797223

#78
**Decor Furniture Gallery**
**Category:** Furniture Store
**Average price:** Expensive
**Area:** South Inner City
**Address:** 14a Wexford St Dublin 2
**Phone:** 353 1 4759010

#79
**Ilac Centre**
**Category:** Shopping Center
**Average price:** Modest
**Area:** North Inner City
**Address:** Henry St Dublin 1
**Phone:** 353 1 8782775

#80
**Silver Trout**
**Category:** Jewelry
**Average price:** Expensive
**Area:** South Inner City
**Address:** 31 S King St Dublin 2
**Phone:** 353 1 6714116

#81
**The Ferocious Mingle Marcade**
**Category:** Flea Market, Market Stall
**Average price:** Expensive
**Area:** Harcourt
**Address:** 60 Camden St Dublin 2
**Phone:** 353 86 0282344

#82
**Muttugly**
**Category:** Shopping, Pet Groomers
**Average price:** Modest
**Area:** Rathgar
**Address:** 111 Ranelagh Village Dublin 6
**Phone:** 353 1 4759449

#83
**Euro 2**
**Category:** Outlet Store
**Average price:** Inexpensive
**Area:** North Inner City
**Address:** 57/58 Moore St Dublin 1
**Phone:** 353 1 8731922

#84
**Urban Outfitters**
**Category:** Men's Clothing,
Women's Clothing, Accessories
**Average price:** Expensive
**Area:** Temple Bar
**Address:** 4 Cecilia St Dublin 2
**Phone:** 353 1 6706202

#85
**Trinity College Library**
**Category:** Bookstore, Mass Media
**Average price:** Inexpensive
**Area:** South Inner City
**Address:** College St Dublin 2
**Phone:** 353 1 6793657

#86
**Marks & Spencer**
**Category:** Department Store
**Average price:** Modest
**Area:** North Inner City
**Address:** 24-29 Mary St Dublin 1
**Phone:** 353 1 8728833

#87
**Ulysses Rare Books**
**Category:** Bookstore
**Average price:** Exclusive
**Area:** Rotunda
**Address:** 10 Duke St Dublin 2
**Phone:** 353 1 6718676

#88
**Decobake**
**Category:** Bakery, Hobby Shop
**Average price:** Modest
**Area:** North Inner City
**Address:** 26 Bachelors Walk Dublin 1
**Phone:** 353 87 47884

#89
**International Books**
**Category:** Bookstore
**Average price:** Inexpensive
**Area:** South Inner City
**Address:** 18 South Frederick St Dublin 2
**Phone:** 353 1 6799375

#90
**Swan Shopping Centre**
**Category:** Shopping Center
**Average price:** Modest
**Area:** Rathmines
**Address:** Lower Rathmines Rd Dublin 6
**Phone:** 353 1 4964566

#91
**Second Avenue**
**Category:** Women's Clothing,
Accessories, Shoe Store
**Average price:** Modest
**Area:** Irishtown
**Address:** 22 Seafort Ave Dublin 4
**Phone:** 353 1 2091110

#92
**Temple Bar Gallery & Studio**
**Category:** Art Gallery
**Average price:** Expensive
**Area:** Temple Bar
**Address:** 5-9 Temple Bar Dublin 2
**Phone:** 353 86 6178026

#93
**Bradys Pharmacy**
**Category:** Drugstore
**Average price:** Modest
**Area:** Harcourt
**Address:** 13 Upper Camden St Dublin 2
**Phone:** 353 1 4751531

#94
**Merrion Shopping Centre**
**Category:** Shopping Center
**Average price:** Modest
**Area:** Merrion
**Address:** Merrion Rd Dublin 4
**Phone:** 44 1209 6959

#95
**Knobs & Knockers**
**Category:** Home Decor, Kitchen & Bath
**Average price:** Expensive
**Area:** South Inner City
**Address:** 19 Nassau St Dublin 2
**Phone:** 353 1 6710288

#96
**Swalk**
**Category:** Cards & Stationery
**Average price:** Modest
**Area:** South Inner City
**Address:** 3 Royal Hibernian Way
Dublin 2
**Phone:** 353 1 6711155

#97
**Claires Accessories UK**
**Category:** Women's Clothing, Accessories
**Average price:** Inexpensive
**Area:** South Inner City
**Address:** 12 Westmoreland St Dublin 2
**Phone:** 353 1 6775240

#98
**Sinn Féin Bookshop**
**Category:** Bookstore, Music & DVDs
**Average price:** Inexpensive
**Area:** Parnell Square
**Address:** 58 Parnell Square Dublin 1
**Phone:** 353 1 8148542

#99
**HMV**
**Category:** Music & DVDs, Vinyl Records,
Television Service Providers
**Average price:** Modest
**Area:** North Inner City
**Address:** 18 Henry St Dublin 1
**Phone:** 353 1 8722905

#100
**French Connection**
**Category:** Women's Clothing
**Average price:** Expensive
**Area:** South Inner City
**Address:** Powerscourt Town Center
Dublin 2
**Phone:** 353 1 6708199

#101
**Runways**
**Category:** Sporting Goods
**Average price:** Expensive
**Area:** Parnell Square
**Address:** 187 Parnell St Dublin 1
**Phone:** 353 1 8146614

#102
**Size?**
**Category:** Shoe Store
**Average price:** Expensive
**Area:** South Inner City
**Address:** 26 Wickow St Dublin 2
**Phone:** 353 1 6771637

#103
**Spindizzy Records**
**Category:** Music & DVDs, Vinyl Records
**Average price:** Modest
**Area:** Rotunda
**Address:** 32 Market Arcade Dublin 2
**Phone:** 353 1 6711711

#104
**Think Bike**
**Category:** Bikes
**Average price:** Modest
**Area:** Rathmines
**Address:** Lower Rathmines Rd Dublin 6
**Phone:** 353 1 4965314

#105
**MakeShop**
**Category:** Hobby Shop
**Average price:** Inexpensive
**Area:** South Inner City
**Address:** Lincoln Place Dublin 2
**Phone:** 353 1 6624416

#106
**Clerys**
**Category:** Department Store
**Average price:** Modest
**Area:** North Inner City
**Address:** 18-27 Lower O'Connell St Dublin 1
**Phone:** 353 1 8786000

#107
**Mary Mall**
**Category:** Shopping Center
**Area:** North Inner City
**Address:** 56 Mary St Dublin 1
**Phone:** 353 87 7699447

#108
**Hickeys Bridal Dress
& Fabric Shop**
**Category:** Women's Clothing
**Average price:** Modest
**Area:** North Inner City
**Address:** 5 Henry St Dublin 1
**Phone:** 353 1 8730714

#109
**Lenehan & Co.**
**Category:** Hardware Store
**Average price:** Modest
**Area:** North Inner City
**Address:** 124 Capel St Dublin 1
**Phone:** 353 1 8730466

#110
**Carousel**
**Category:** Vintage,
Consignment, Women's Clothing
**Average price:** Modest
**Area:** South Inner City
**Address:** 20 Exchequer St Dublin 2
**Phone:** 353 1 6778713

#111
**Article**
**Category:** Furniture Store, Gift Shop
**Average price:** Modest
**Area:** South Inner City
**Address:** 1st Fl, South William St Dublin 2
**Phone:** 353 1 6799268

#112
**The R.A.G.E.
Record Art Game Emporium**
**Category:** Vinyl Records, Music & DVDs,
Videos, Video Game Rental
**Average price:** Expensive
**Area:** South Inner City
**Address:** 16B Fade St Dublin 2
**Phone:** 353 1 6779594

#113
**House of Fraser**
**Category:** Department Store
**Average price:** Expensive
**Area:** Windy Arbour
**Address:** Unit 1, Dundrum
Shopping Centre Dublin 16
**Phone:** 353 1 2991400

#114
**A/Wear**
**Category:** Women's Clothing, Accessories
**Average price:** Modest
**Area:** South Inner City
**Address:** Grafton St Dublin 2
**Phone:** 353 1 4724960

#115
**Decwells DIY**
**Category:** Electronics, Hardware Store
**Average price:** Expensive
**Area:** South Inner City
**Address:** 60 South Great
Georges St Dublin 2
**Phone:** 353 1 4781377

#116
**H&M**
**Category:** Women's Clothing,
Men's Clothing, Children's Clothing
**Average price:** Modest
**Area:** South Inner City
**Address:** 35-39 S King St Dublin 2
**Phone:** 353 1 8044729

#117
**Konfusion**
**Category:** Women's Clothing, Accessories
**Average price:** Modest
**Area:** Temple Bar
**Address:** 5a Crown Alley Dublin 2
**Phone:** 353 1 7071760

#118
**Office**
**Category:** Shoe Store
**Average price:** Modest
**Area:** North Inner City
**Address:** 6 Henry St Dublin 1
**Phone:** 353 1 8748250

#119
**Elverys Sports**
**Category:** Sporting Goods
**Average price:** Modest
**Area:** South Inner City
**Address:** 19 Suffolk St Dublin 2
**Phone:** 353 1 6791555

#120
**Designist**
**Category:** Concept Shop
**Average price:** Expensive
**Area:** South Inner City
**Address:** 68 South Great
Georges St Dublin 2
**Phone:** 353 1 4758534

#121
**P & K Cycles**
**Category:** Bikes
**Area:** The Liberties
**Address:** Patrick St Dublin 8
**Phone:** 353 1 4734002

#122
**China Blue**
**Category:** Shoe Store
**Average price:** Modest
**Area:** Temple Bar
**Address:** Merchants Arch Dublin 2
**Phone:** 353 1 6718785

#123
**Zara**
**Category:** Women's Clothing,
Men's Clothing
**Average price:** Modest
**Area:** North Inner City
**Address:** 46/47 Henry St Dublin 1
**Phone:** 353 1 8045900

#124
**Clarks**
**Category:** Shoe Store
**Average price:** Modest
**Area:** South Inner City
**Address:** 85 Grafton St Dublin 2
**Phone:** 353 1 6711257

#125
**The Bag Warehouse**
**Category:** Luggage
**Average price:** Expensive
**Area:** North Inner City
**Address:** 10 Talbot St Dublin 1
**Phone:** 353 1 8731065

#126
**Dunnes Store**
**Category:** Department Store
**Average price:** Modest
**Area:** North Inner City
**Address:** Henry St Dublin 1
**Phone:** 353 1 8146224

#127
**Lynch Computer Repair**
**Category:** Computers
**Average price:** Modest
**Area:** Temple Bar
**Address:** 2 Merchants Arch Dublin 2
**Phone:** 353 1 5485324

#128
**Jam Art Factory**
**Category:** Arts & Crafts
**Area:** Temple Bar
**Address:** 14 Crown Alley Dublin
**Phone:** 353 1 6165671

#129
**Casa Rebelde**
**Category:** Men's Clothing, Soccer
**Area:** Temple Bar
**Address:** Crow St Dublin 2
**Phone:** 353 1 6779234

#130
**Penneys**
**Category:** Department Store
**Average price:** Inexpensive
**Area:** South Inner City
**Address:** Dundrum Shopping Centre Dublin
**Phone:** 353 1 2987410

#131
**Find**
**Category:** Vintage,
Consignment, Antiques
**Average price:** Modest
**Area:** Temple Bar
**Address:** Unit 1 Sauls Court Dublin 8
**Phone:** 353 86 6078667

#132
**Parfumarija**
**Category:** Perfume
**Average price:** Expensive
**Area:** South Inner City
**Address:** 25 Westbury
Shopping Mall Dublin 2
**Phone:** 353 1 6710255

#133
**Sweeney O'Rourke**
**Category:** Kitchen & Bath
**Average price:** Modest
**Area:** South Inner City
**Address:** 34 pearse St Dublin 2
**Phone:** 353 1 6777212

#134
**Hicken Lighting**
**Category:** Interior Design, Lighting
Fixtures & Equipment, Furniture Store
**Area:** Thomas St
**Address:** 17 Lower Bridge St Dublin 8
**Phone:** 353 1 6777882

#135
**Swenys Pharmacy**
**Category:** Drugstore
**Average price:** Modest
**Area:** South Inner City
**Address:** 1 Lincoln Place Dublin 2
**Phone:** 353 1 6762053

#136
**Wexford St Pharmacy**
**Category:** Drugstore
**Average price:** Modest
**Area:** South Inner City
**Address:** Wexford St Dublin 2
**Phone:** 353 1 4750105

#137
**The Constant Knitter**
**Category:** Knitting Supplies
**Average price:** Modest
**Area:** The Liberties
**Address:** 88 Francis St Dublin 8
**Phone:** 353 87 9967197

#138
**The Cat's Meow**
**Category:** Vintage, Consignment
**Average price:** Modest
**Area:** The Liberties
**Address:** 74 Francis St Dublin 8
**Phone:** 353 86 8158161

#139
**Lynch B & Sons**
**Category:** Men's Clothing
**Average price:** Modest
**Area:** Harcourt
**Address:** 62 Lower Camden St Dublin 2
**Phone:** 353 1 4751642

#140
**Corrigans Pharmacy**
**Category:** Drugstore
**Area:** Marino, Clontarf
**Address:** 80 Malahide Rd Dublin 3
**Phone:** 353 1 8338803

#141
**Business Management Systems**
**Category:** Computers
**Area:** Greenhills
**Address:** Greenhills Rd Dublin 12
**Phone:** 353 1 4505277

#142
**Hugo Boss**
**Category:** Men's Clothing,
Women's Clothing
**Average price:** Expensive
**Area:** Dundrum
**Address:** House of Fraser Dublin
**Phone:** 353 1 2991437

#143
**Adams**
**Category:** Children's Clothing
**Area:** Stillorgan
**Address:** Stillorgan Shopping
Centre Dublin 4
**Phone:** 353 1 2836636

#144
**Rathfarnham Shopping Centre**
**Category:** Shopping Center
**Average price:** Modest
**Area:** Rathfarnham
**Address:** 20e Rathfarnham Sc Dublin 14
**Phone:** 353 1 4953177

#145
**Powerscourt Townhouse Centre**
**Category:** Shopping Center
**Average price:** Expensive
**Area:** South Inner City
**Address:** 59 S William St Dublin 2
**Phone:** 353 1 6794144

#146
**Music Maker Ltd**
**Category:** Musical Instruments
**Average price:** Expensive
**Area:** South Inner City
**Address:** 29 Exchequer St Dublin 2
**Phone:** 353 1 6779004

#147
**Mira Mira**
**Category:** Accessories, Gift Shop, Toy Store
**Average price:** Expensive
**Area:** Irishtown
**Address:** 3 Sandymount Green Dublin 4
**Phone:** 353 1 2196668

#148
**Gallery Quay Pharmacy**
**Category:** Drugstore
**Average price:** Modest
**Area:** Grand Canal Dock
**Address:** Unit G6 Gallery Quay Dublin 2
**Phone:** 353 1 7071883

#149
**Irish Design Shop**
**Category:** Arts & Crafts
**Average price:** Modest
**Area:** South Inner City
**Address:** 41 Drury St Dublin 2
**Phone:** 353 1 6798871

#150
**Specsavers Opticians**
**Category:** Eyewear & Opticians
**Average price:** Modest
**Area:** South Inner City
**Address:** 112 Grafton St Dublin 2
**Phone:** 353 1 6776969

#151
**Carphone Warehouse**
**Category:** Mobile Phones
**Average price:** Modest
**Area:** Rathgar
**Address:** 290 Lower Rathmines Rd Dublin 6
**Phone:** 353 1 4970121

#152
**House Of Ireland**
**Category:** Home & Garden,
Flowers & Gifts
**Average price:** Expensive
**Area:** South Inner City
**Address:** 37 Nassau St
Dublin 2
**Phone:** 353 1 6711111

#153
**T. Bear & Co.**
**Category:** Toy Store
**Average price:** Modest
**Area:** Malahide
**Address:** 2 Townyard Ln Dublin 2
**Phone:** 353 1 8061866

#154
**Se Si**
**Category:** Accessories,
Women's Clothing
**Average price:** Modest
**Area:** Temple Bar
**Address:** 11 Fownes St Upper Dublin 2
**Phone:** 353 1 6774779

#155
**Gallery of Photography**
**Category:** Art Gallery
**Average price:** Modest
**Area:** Temple Bar
**Address:** Meeting House Square Dublin 2
**Phone:** 353 1 6714654

#156
**Monto**
**Category:** Vintage, Consignment
**Average price:** Inexpensive
**Area:** Parnell Square
**Address:** Parnell St Dublin 1
**Phone:** 353 1 8720205

#157
**E-Smoke Ireland**
**Category:** Electronics
**Area:** Palmerstown
**Address:** 28 Palmers Crescent Dublin 1
**Phone:** 353 86 8955041

#158
**Yellow Brick Rd**
**Category:** Jewelry, Bookstore
**Average price:** Inexpensive
**Area:** North Inner City
**Address:** 8 Bachelors Walk Dublin 1
**Phone:** 353 1 8730177

#159
**Dubray Books**
**Category:** Bookstore
**Average price:** Modest
**Area:** South Inner City
**Address:** 24 Grafton St Dublin 2
**Phone:** 353 1 6775568

#160
**Rothar Bike Cafe**
**Category:** Coffee & Tea, Bikes
**Average price:** Modest
**Area:** South Inner City
**Address:** 16 Fade St Dublin 2
**Phone:** 353 1 6772233

#161
**Into IT**
**Category:** Computers
**Average price:** Inexpensive
**Area:** South Inner City
**Address:** 39 Westland Row Dublin 2
**Phone:** 353 1 6789856

#162
**La Catedral Studio**
**& The Back Loft**
**Category:** Art Gallery, Venues,
Event Space
**Average price:** Inexpensive
**Area:** Thomas St
**Address:** 7/11 St. Augustine St Dublin 8
**Phone:** 353 87 2753944

#163
**Gas & Electric Centre**
**Category:** Appliances
**Average price:** Modest
**Area:** Harcourt
**Address:** 12 Camden St Dublin 2
**Phone:** 353 1 4751505

#164
**The Orchard**
**Category:** Newspapers & Magazines
**Average price:** Inexpensive
**Area:** Rathgar
**Address:** 22 Sandford Rd Dublin 6
**Phone:** 353 1 4972936

#165
**Baggot Framing**
**Category:** Framing
**Average price:** Modest
**Area:** Baggot St
**Address:** 13 Eastmoreland Place Dublin 4
**Phone:** 353 1 6606063

#166
**Churchtown Store**
**Category:** Hardware Store
**Average price:** Modest
**Area:** Churchtown
**Address:** 5 Braemor Rd Dublin 14
**Phone:** 353 1 2987778

#167
**Louis Copeland & Sons**
**Category:** Men's Clothing
**Average price:** Exclusive
**Area:** North Inner City
**Address:** 39-41 Capel St Dublin 1
**Phone:** 353 1 8720055

#168
**Serendipity Kids**
**Category:** Baby Gear & Furniture
**Average price:** Expensive
**Area:** Rathgar
**Address:** 52 Ranelagh Village Dublin 6
**Phone:** 353 1 4968489

#169
**Outdoor Adventure Store**
**Category:** Outdoor Gear
**Average price:** Modest
**Area:** North Inner City
**Address:** 34 / 35 Upper Liffey St Dublin 1
**Phone:** 353 1 8725177

#170
**Connolly Books**
**Category:** Bookstore
**Area:** Temple Bar
**Address:** 43 East Essex St Dublin 2
**Phone:** 353 1 6708707

#171
**Patagonia Outlet**
**Category:** Outdoor Gear, Outlet Store
**Average price:** Modest
**Area:** South Inner City
**Address:** 26/28 Exchequer St Dublin 2
**Phone:** 353 1 6705748

#172
**Early Learning Centre**
**Category:** Toy Store
**Average price:** Modest
**Area:** North Inner City
**Address:** Henry St Dublin 1
**Phone:** 353 1 8731945

#173
**Mr Middleton Garden Shop**
**Category:** Home & Garden
**Average price:** Modest
**Area:** North Inner City
**Address:** 58 Mary St Dublin 1
**Phone:** 353 1 8731118

#174
**Goodwin's Musical Instruments**
**Category:** Musical Instruments
**Area:** North Inner City
**Address:** 134 Capel St Dublin 2
**Phone:** 353 1 8730846

#175
**The Company Of Books**
**Category:** Bookstore
**Area:** Rathgar
**Address:** 96 Ranelagh Village Dublin 6
**Phone:** 353 1 4975413

#176
**Dunnes Store**
**Category:** Grocery, Department Store
**Average price:** Modest
**Area:** Crumlin
**Address:** Cromwellsfort Rd Dublin 12
**Phone:** 353 1 4560400

#177
**BT2**
**Category:** Department Store
**Average price:** Expensive
**Area:** South Inner City
**Address:** 28 29 Grafton St Dublin 2
**Phone:** 353 1 6056707

#178
**Muji**
**Category:** Kitchen & Bath,
Cards & Stationery, Home Decor
**Average price:** Modest
**Area:** South Inner City
**Address:** 5 Chatham St Dublin 2
**Phone:** 353 1 6794591

#179
**Maplin Electronics**
**Category:** Electronics
**Average price:** Exclusive
**Area:** North Inner City
**Address:** 1-4 Jervis St Dublin 1
**Phone:** 353 1 8782388

#180
**Next**
**Category:** Women's Clothing
**Average price:** Modest
**Area:** South Inner City
**Address:** 68 Grafton St Dublin 2
**Phone:** 353 1 6793300

#181
**Smyths Toys**
**& Computer Games**
**Category:** Toy Store
**Average price:** Modest
**Area:** North Inner City
**Address:** Jervis St Dublin 1
**Phone:** 353 1 8782878

#182
**Eurospar**
**Category:** Department Store
**Average price:** Modest
**Area:** Kilmainham
**Address:** The TramYard Dublin 8
**Phone:** 353 1 4733740

#183
**Reads of Nassau St.**
**Category:** Bookstore, Art Supplies,
Cards & Stationery
**Average price:** Inexpensive
**Area:** South Inner City
**Address:** 24/26 Nassau St Dublin 2
**Phone:** 353 1 6796011

#184
**Walton's Music**
**Category:** Musical Instruments
**Average price:** Modest
**Area:** Rotunda
**Address:** 2 N Frederick St Dublin 1
**Phone:** 353 1 8747805

#185
**TK Maxx**
**Category:** Accessories, Men's Clothing,
Women's Clothing
**Average price:** Expensive
**Area:** Blanchardstown
**Address:** Blanchardstown Town
Centre Dublin 15
**Phone:** 353 1 8219410

#186
**Belfield Bike Shop**
**Category:** Department Store
**Average price:** Modest
**Area:** Belfield
**Address:** Belfield House Dublin 4
**Phone:** 353 1 7161697

#187
**Karen Millen**
**Category:** Women's Clothing
**Average price:** Expensive
**Area:** South Inner City
**Address:** 72 Grafton St Dublin 2
**Phone:** 353 1 6339546

#188
**Great Outdoors Watersports**
**Category:** Outdoor Gear, Boating, Diving
**Average price:** Expensive
**Area:** South Inner City
**Address:** Johnson's Place Dublin 2
**Phone:** 353 1 6794293

#189
**Monsoon Accessorize**
**Category:** Accessories,
Children's Clothing
**Average price:** Expensive
**Area:** South Inner City
**Address:** 38 Grafton St Dublin 2
**Phone:** 353 1 6717322

#190
**Coolmine Carpet**
**Category:** Home & Garden
**Area:** Blanchardstown
**Address:** U5 Coolmine Industrial
Estate Dublin 15
**Phone:** 353 1 8206627

#191
**Fun Place**
**Category:** Costumes
**Average price:** Modest
**Area:** South Inner City
**Address:** 52 S King St Dublin 2
**Phone:** 353 1 6778817

#192
**Michael Barrie Menswear**
**Category:** Men's Clothing
**Average price:** Modest
**Area:** South Inner City
**Address:** 20 Duke St Dublin 2
**Phone:** 353 1 6715265

#193
**Merchants Yard**
**Category:** Market Stall
**Area:** East Wall
**Address:** East Wall Rd Dublin 1
**Phone:** 353 1 8199999

#194
**Boots**
**Category:** Drugstore,
Cosmetics & Beauty
**Average price:** Modest
**Area:** Rathmines
**Address:** 302 Lower Rathmines Rd Dublin 6
**Phone:** 353 31 4969700

#195
**Millets Camping**
**Category:** Outdoor Gear
**Average price:** Modest
**Area:** North Inner City
**Address:** 61-62 Mary St Dublin 1
**Phone:** 353 1 8732250

#196
**Fat Face**
**Category:** Women's Clothing,
Men's Clothing, Outdoor Gear
**Average price:** Modest
**Area:** South Inner City
**Address:** 31 Exchequer St Dublin 2
**Phone:** 353 1 6772415

#197
**Office**
**Category:** Shoe Store
**Average price:** Expensive
**Area:** South Inner City
**Address:** 7 Grafton St Dublin 2
**Phone:** 353 1 6709960

#198
**Back From The Future**
**Category:** Computers
**Average price:** Expensive
**Area:** South Inner City
**Address:** 77 Aungier St Dublin 2
**Phone:** 353 1 4757177

#199
**The Great Outdoors**
**Category:** Sports Wear, Outdoor Gear
**Average price:** Expensive
**Area:** South Inner City
**Address:** Chatham St Dublin 2
**Phone:** 353 1 6794293

#200
**Barry Doyle Design Jewellers**
**Category:** Jewelry
**Average price:** Expensive
**Area:** Ballybough
**Address:** 1st Floor 30 Georges St
Arcade Dublin 2
**Phone:** 353 1 6712838

#201
**Dunnes Store**
**Category:** Grocery, Beer, Wine, Spirits,
Shopping Center
**Average price:** Modest
**Area:** Cabinteely
**Address:** Cornelscourt Shopping
Centre Dublin 18
**Phone:** 353 1 2892677

#202
**Fran & Jane**
**Category:** Women's Clothing,
Jewelry, Accessories
**Average price:** Expensive
**Area:** IFSC
**Address:** CHQ Dublin 1
**Phone:** 353 1 6702640

#203
**Trinity College Library Shop**
**Category:** Bookstore
**Average price.** Modest
**Area:** South Inner City
**Address:** Trinity College Dublin Dublin 2
**Phone:** 353 1 6081171

#204
**Liffey Bag Warehouse**
**Category:** Shoe Store
**Average price:** Inexpensive
**Area:** North Inner City
**Address:** 27 Lower Liffey St Dublin 1
**Phone:** 353 1 8722171

#205
**The North Face Store**
**Category:** Sports Wear, Outdoor Gear
**Average price:** Expensive
**Area:** Temple Bar
**Address:** 17/18 Temple Lane
South Dublin 2
**Phone:** 353 1 6727088

#206
**Medipharm**
**Category:** Drugstore, Nutritionists
**Average price:** Modest
**Area:** South Inner City
**Address:** 16 S Great George's St Dublin 2
**Phone:** 353 1 6719765

#207
**Mrs Quins Charity Shop**
**Category:** Thrift Store
**Average price:** Inexpensive
**Area:** Terenure
**Address:** 2 Terenure Rd North Dublin 6w
**Phone:** 353 87 1394349

#208
**Royal Hibernian Way**
**Category:** Shopping Center
**Area:** South Inner City
**Address:** Dawson St Dublin 2
**Phone:** 353 1 6795919

#209
**Clarks**
**Category:** Shoe Store
**Average price:** Modest
**Area:** North Inner City
**Address:** 43 O'Connell St Dublin 1
**Phone:** 353 1 8727665

#210
**Mark's Models**
**Category:** Hobby Shop
**Area:** South Inner City
**Address:** 14 Hawkins St Dublin 2
**Phone:** 353 1 6716000

#211
**IFI Film Shop**
**Category:** Music & DVDs, Bookstore
**Average price:** Modest
**Area:** Temple Bar
**Address:** 6 Eustace St Dublin 2
**Phone:** 353 1 6795727

#212
**9 Crow St.**
**Category:** Vintage, Consignment
**Average price:** Modest
**Area:** North Inner City
**Address:** 5 Ormond Quay Dublin 1
**Phone:** 353 1 5510223

#213
**Dirty Fabulous**
**Category:** Jewelry, Bridal,
Women's Clothing
**Area:** South Inner City
**Address:** 21 Wicklow St Dublin 2
**Phone:** 353 1 6111842

#214
**ThunderSolas**
**Category:** Leather Goods, Accessories
**Average price:** Modest
**Area:** Temple Bar
**Address:** 2 Cow's Lane Dublin 2
**Phone:** 353 1 6798713

#215
**Sisley**
**Category:** Women's Clothing,
Men's Clothing
**Average price:** Modest
**Area:** South Inner City
**Address:** 88-95 Grafton St Dublin 2
**Phone:** 353 1 6728698

#216
**House Of Names**
**Category:** Hobby Shop, Local Flavor
**Average price:** Expensive
**Area:** South Inner City
**Address:** 26 Nassau St Dublin 2
**Phone:** 353 1 6797287

#217
**MJ Foley & Son**
**Category:** Drugstore
**Average price:** Modest
**Area:** Rotunda
**Address:** 136 Parnell St Dublin 1
**Phone:** 353 1 8746972

#218
**Timepiece**
**Category:** Watches, Antiques
**Area:** Clanbrassil St
**Address:** 57 - 58 Patrick St Dublin 8
**Phone:** 353 1 4540774

#219
**A4 Art**
**Category:** Art Supplies
**Average price:** Inexpensive
**Area:** Thomas St
**Address:** 88 Thomas St Dublin 8
**Phone:** 353 1 6854310

#220
**Block T**
**Category:** Music Venues, Art Gallery
**Area:** Smithfield
**Address:** 1-6 Haymarket Dublin 7
**Phone:** 353 1 5351014

#221
**Oriental Rugs**
**Category:** Antiques, Furniture Store,
Home Decor
**Area:** The Liberties
**Address:** 104 Francis St Dublin 8
**Phone:** 353 1 4531222

#222
**Gallery Zozimus**
**Category:** Art Gallery
**Average price:** Expensive
**Area:** The Liberties
**Address:** 56 Francis St Dublin 8
**Phone:** 353 1 4539057

#223
**EO Ireland**
**Category:** Cosmetics & Beauty
**Average price:** Expensive
**Area:** South Inner City
**Address:** Pearse St Dublin
**Phone:** 353 87 6788463

#224
**Coppa Cafe**
**Category:** Art Gallery, Coffee & Tea
**Average price:** Modest
**Area:** South Inner City
**Address:** 15 Ely Place Dublin 2
**Phone:** 353 1 6618411

#225
**Phelan's Pharmacy**
**Category:** Drugstore
**Area:** Portobello
**Address:** 22 Clanbrassil St
Lower Dublin 8
**Phone:** 353 1 4734083

#226
**Edge Hardware**
**Category:** Hardware Store
**Area:** Marino
**Address:** 2 Fairview Dublin 3
**Phone:** 353 1 8747579

#227
**Bee Cycles**
**Category:** Bikes
**Average price:** Modest
**Area:** South Circular Rd
**Address:** 380 South Circular Rd Dublin 8
**Phone:** 353 86 8895487

#228
**O'Meara Camping Centre**
**Category:** Outdoor Gear
**Average price:** Modest
**Area:** Crumlin
**Address:** Crumlin Rd Dublin
**Phone:** 353 1 4534070

#229
**Lady Umbrella**
**Category:** Women's Clothing
**Average price:** Modest
**Area:** Marino
**Address:** 200 Grace Park Heights Dublin 9
**Phone:** 353 86 8894726

#230
**Harvey Nichols**
**Category:** Department Store
**Average price:** Exclusive
**Area:** Clonskeagh
**Address:** Dundrum Town Centre Dublin 16
**Phone:** 353 1 2910488

#231
**Newlands Garden Centre**
**Category:** Home & Garden
**Average price:** Modest
**Area:** Clondalkin
**Address:** New Rd Dublin
**Phone:** 353 1 4592013

#232
**Peterson of Dublin**
**Category:** Tobacco Shop
**Average price:** Expensive
**Area:** South Inner City
**Address:** 48-49 Nassau St Dublin 2
**Phone:** 353 1 6714652

#233
**Schuh**
**Category:** Shoe Store
**Average price:** Expensive
**Area:** Palmerstown
**Address:** U49 Liffey Valley Centre
**Phone:** 353 1 6266100

#234
**Vision Express**
**Category:** Eyewear & Opticians
**Average price:** Modest
**Area:** North Inner City
**Address:** Henry St Dublin 1
**Phone:** 353 1 8732477

#235
**Game Stop**
**Category:** Videos, Video Game Rental
**Average price:** Exclusive
**Area:** North Inner City
**Address:** Henry St Dublin 1
**Phone:** 353 1 8725488

#236
**Gerry Keane**
**Category:** Hardware Store
**Area:** North Inner City
**Address:** 14 Talbot St Dublin 1
**Phone:** 353 1 8745783

#237
**Appassionata Shop**
**Category:** Florist
**Average price:** Expensive
**Area:** South Inner City
**Address:** 29 Drury St Dublin 2
**Phone:** 353 1 6729425

#238
**T.M. Lewin**
**Category:** Men's Clothing
**Average price:** Modest
**Area:** South Inner City
**Address:** 32-33 S Anne St Dublin 2
**Phone:** 353 1 0339781

#239
**Molton Brown**
**Category:** Shopping
**Average price:** Expensive
**Area:** South Inner City
**Address:** Wickow St Dublin 2
**Phone:** 353 1 6799504

#240
**Pearse St. Hardware**
**Category:** Hardware Store
**Average price:** Inexpensive
**Area:** Grand Canal Dock
**Address:** 109 Pearse St Dublin 2
**Phone:** 353 1 6751980

#241
**Hampton Books**
**Category:** Bookstore
**Average price:** Modest
**Area:** Milltown
**Address:** 93a Morehampton Rd Dublin 4
**Phone:** 353 1 6673072

#242
**Murtagh's Hardware & DIY**
**Category:** Hardware Store, Nursery,
Gardening, Home Decor
**Average price:** Modest
**Area:** Irishtown
**Address:** 91 Sandymount Rd Dublin 4
**Phone:** 353 1 6617297

#243
**Oasis Florist**
**Category:** Florist
**Area:** Terenure
**Address:** 88 Terenure Rd North Dublin 6
**Phone:** 353 1 4900112

#244
**Bradley's Pharmacy**
**Category:** Photography Store, Drugstore,
Cosmetics & Beauty
**Average price:** Modest
**Area:** Kimmage
**Address:** 2a Fortfield Rd Dublin 6w
**Phone:** 353 1 4908098

#245
**Books Upstairs**
**Category:** Bookstore
**Average price:** Modest
**Area:** Santry
**Address:** Unit 25, Omnipark Shopping
Centre Dublin 9
**Phone:** 353 1 8421210

#246
**May Fly**
**Category:** Jewelry, Accessories
**Average price:** Modest
**Area:** Temple Bar
**Address:** 11, Fownes St Upper Dublin 2
**Phone:** 353 86 3764189

#247
**Safari Crafts**
**Category:** Jewelry, Women's Clothing,
Flowers & Gifts
**Average price:** Inexpensive
**Area:** North Inner City
**Address:** 29 Lower Liffey St Dublin 1
**Phone:** 353 1 8724761

#248
**Beads and Bling**
**Category:** Fashion
**Average price:** Expensive
**Area:** Temple Bar
**Address:** 34 Wellington Quay Dublin 2
**Phone:** 353 1 6337814

#249
**Eager Beaver**
**Category:** Vintage,
Consignment, Accessories
**Average price:** Modest
**Area:** Temple Bar
**Address:** 17 Crown Alley Dublin 2
**Phone:** 353 1 6773342

#250
**Bang & Olufsen**
**Category:** Electronics, Appliances
**Average price:** Exclusive
**Area:** Ballsbridge
**Address:** 6 Main St Dublin 4
**Phone:** 353 1 2602404

#251
**The Bike Institute**
**Category:** Vocational, Technical School
**Area:** Rotunda
**Address:** 22 Lower Dorset St Dublin 1
**Phone:** 353 83 1537861

#252
**Wheelworx Bike & Tri Shop**
**Category:** Sports Wear,
Outdoor Gear, Bikes
**Average price:** Exclusive
**Area:** Lucan
**Address:** Unit 48, Fonthill Retail Park
**Phone:** 353 1 6201000

#253
**MacDonalds**
**Category:** Auto Parts & Supplies, Bikes
**Area:** South Inner City
**Address:** 38 Wexford St Dublin 2
**Phone:** 353 1 4752586

#254
**Nutgrove Shopping Centre**
**Category:** Shopping Center
**Average price:** Modest
**Area:** Rathfarnham
**Address:** Nutgrove Avenue Dublin
**Phone:** 353 1 4933289

#255
**Enable Ireland**
**Category:** Thrift Store
**Average price:** Inexpensive
**Area:** South Inner City
**Address:** 8 South Great
Georges St Dublin 2
**Phone:** 353 1 4782763

#256
**Bose**
**Category:** Electronics
**Area:** Dundrum
**Address:** Dundrum Town Centre Dublin 14
**Phone:** 353 1 2965174

#257
**Mothercare**
**Category:** Children's Clothing,
Baby Gear & Furniture
**Average price:** Modest
**Area:** North Inner City
**Address:** Jervis St Dublin 1
**Phone:** 353 1 8781184

#258
**Ann Summers**
**Category:** Lingerie, Adult
**Average price:** Modest
**Area:** North Inner City
**Address:** 30-31 Lower O'Connell St Dublin 1
**Phone:** 353 1 8781385

#259
**The Art & Hobby Shop**
**Category:** Hobby Shop, Art Supplies
**Average price:** Modest
**Area:** North Inner City
**Address:** Jervis St Shopping Centre Dublin 1
**Phone:** 353 1 8745312

#260
**Ecco Shoes**
**Category:** Shoe Store
**Average price:** Expensive
**Area:** South Inner City
**Address:** 11 Wicklow St Dublin 2
**Phone:** 353 1 6798714

#261
**Sweater Shop**
**Category:** Women's Clothing,
Men's Clothing
**Average price:** Modest
**Area:** South Inner City
**Address:** 30 Nassau St Dublin 2
**Phone:** 353 1 6712292

#262
**The Bargain Shop @ Arnotts**
**Category:** Furniture Store
**Average price:** Inexpensive
**Area:** North Inner City
**Address:** Middle Abbey St Dublin 1
**Phone:** 353 1 8050400

#263
**Pen Place**
**Category:** Office Equipment,
Cards & Stationery
**Average price:** Expensive
**Area:** Dún Laoghaire
**Address:** Dún Laoghaire Shopping Ctr
**Phone:** 353 1 2805020

#264
**Johnstons Court Vintage Emporium**
**Category:** Antiques, Jewelry
**Area:** South Inner City
**Address:** Johnstons Court Dublin 2
**Phone:** 353 1 6706825

#265
**City Cycles**
**Category:** Bikes
**Area:** Collins Barracks
**Address:** 47 Blackhall Pl Dublin 7
**Phone:** 353 1 6400900

#266
**Vincent's**
**Category:** Thrift Store
**Average price:** Inexpensive
**Area:** Marino
**Address:** 2a Fairview Dublin 3
**Phone:** 353 1 8550022

#267
**Science Gallery Dublin Shop**
**Category:** Electronics, Bookstore
**Area:** South Inner City
**Address:** Pearse St Dublin 2
**Phone:** 353 1 8964131

#268
**Pull and Bear**
**Category:** Women's Clothing,
Men's Clothing
**Average price:** Expensive
**Area:** North Inner City
**Address:** 22-23 Henry St Dublin 1
**Phone:** 353 1 8897945

#269
**River Island**
**Category:** Fashion
**Average price:** Modest
**Area:** North Inner City
**Address:** 12 Henry St Dublin 1
**Phone:** 353 1 8725273

#270
**Celtic Note**
**Category:** Musical Instruments,
Music & DVDs
**Average price:** Modest
**Area:** South Inner City
**Address:** 14/15 Nassau Sreet Dublin 2
**Phone:** 353 1 6704157

#271
**Bermingham Cameras**
**Category:** Photography Store
**Average price:** Expensive
**Area:** South Inner City
**Address:** 9 Burgh Quay Dublin 2
**Phone:** 353 1 6772205

#272
**Goodwill Industries**
**Category:** Thrift Store
**Average price:** Inexpensive
**Area:** North Inner City
**Address:** 142 Capel St Dublin 1
**Phone:** 353 1 8725037

#273
**Buffalo**
**Category:** Shoe Store
**Average price:** Expensive
**Area:** South Inner City
**Address:** 16 Exchequer St Dublin 2
**Phone:** 353 1 6712492

#274
**Aldo**
**Category:** Shoe Store
**Average price:** Modest
**Area:** South Inner City
**Address:** 83 Grafton St Dublin 2
**Phone:** 353 1 6799338

#275
**Elysian Brows**
**Category:** Eyelash Service,
Cosmetics & Beauty, Hair Removal
**Average price:** Modest
**Area:** South Inner City
**Address:** 36/37 South William St Dublin 2
**Phone:** 353 1 8883666

#276
**Tribe**
**Category:** Men's Clothing,
Shoe Store, Sports Wear
**Average price:** Expensive
**Area:** South Inner City
**Address:** Unit 109, First Floor Dublin 2
**Phone:** 353 1 4750311

#277
**H&M**
**Category:** Women's Clothing,
Men's Clothing, Accessories
**Average price:** Modest
**Area:** North Inner City
**Address:** Henry St Dublin 1
**Phone:** 353 1 8727206

#278
**Rathmines Pharmacy**
**Category:** Drugstore
**Average price:** Modest
**Area:** Rathmines
**Address:** 114 Lwr Rathmines Rd Dublin 6
**Phone:** 353 1 4979999

#279
**Next**
**Category:** Men's Clothing,
Women's Clothing
**Average price:** Modest
**Area:** Clonskeagh
**Address:** Dundrum Town Centre Dublin 16
**Phone:** 353 31 205131

#280
**L'Occitane**
**Category:** Cosmetics & Beauty
**Area:** Sandyford
**Address:** Sandyford Rd Dublin 16
**Phone:** 353 1 2963388

#281
**Moore St Mall**
**Category:** Electronics, Ethnic Food,
Hair Salon
**Average price:** Inexpensive
**Area:** North Inner City
**Address:** 58-66 Parnell St., Dublin 1
**Phone:** 353 1 8733416

#282
**Kling**
**Category:** Women's Clothing
**Average price:** Modest
**Area:** North Inner City
**Address:** 2 Blooms Lane Dublin 1
**Phone:** 353 1 8733550

#283
**Boudoir by Celine C**
**Category:** Jewelry
**Average price:** Expensive
**Area:** South Inner City
**Address:** 7 Pembroke Lane Dublin 4
**Phone:** 353 1 6689886

#284
**Ted Baker**
**Category:** Men's Clothing, Shoe Store,
Women's Clothing
**Average price:** Exclusive
**Area:** South Inner City
**Address:** 42 Grafton St Dublin 2
**Phone:** 353 1 8814111

#285
**The CHQ Building**
**Category:** Shopping Center
**Average price:** Expensive
**Area:** IFSC
**Address:** IFSC, Dublin Docklands Dublin
**Phone:** 353 1 6736054

#286
**Claire's Accessories**
**Category:** Women's Clothing,
Accessories, Jewelry
**Average price:** Modest
**Area:** South Inner City
**Address:** C13 14 St Stephens
Green Dublin 2
**Phone:** 353 1 4784232

#287
**Books On The Green**
**Category:** Bookstore
**Average price:** Modest
**Area:** Irishtown
**Address:** 2 Seafort Ave Dublin 4
**Phone:** 353 1 2837909

#288
**New Look**
**Category:** Shoe Store
**Average price:** Inexpensive
**Area:** Tallaght
**Address:** 242 The Square Town
Centre Dublin 24
**Phone:** 353 1 4623538

#289
**Woodworkers & Hobbies Supply**
**Category:** Home Decor, Hobby Shop
**Average price:** Modest
**Area:** Harold's Cross
**Address:** 1A Mt Tallent Ave Dublin 6w
**Phone:** 353 1 4901968

#290
**Homestore & More**
**Category:** Kitchen & Bath, Home Decor
**Average price:** Modest
**Area:** Palmerstown
**Address:** Liffey Valley Fonthill Retail
Business Park Dublin
**Phone:** 353 1 6208496

#291
**Gorta**
**Category:** Thrift Store, Fashion
**Average price:** Inexpensive
**Area:** North Inner City
**Address:** 32 Lower Liffey St Dublin 1
**Phone:** 353 1 8731155

#292
**Hickey's Pharmacy**
**Category:** Drugstore
**Average price:** Modest
**Area:** North Inner City
**Address:** 55 Lower O'Connell St
Dublin 1
**Phone:** 353 1 8730427

#293
**Temple Bar Pharmacy**
**Category:** Drugstore
**Average price:** Modest
**Area:** Temple Bar
**Address:** 21 Essex St East Dublin 2
**Phone:** 353 1 6709751

#294
**Michael Guineys**
**Category:** Home & Garden
**Average price:** Inexpensive
**Area:** North Inner City
**Address:** 4 North Earl St Dublin 1
**Phone:** 353 1 8788944

#295
**All City**
Category: Vinyl Records, Art Supplies
Average price: Inexpensive
Area: Temple Bar
Address: 4 Crow St Dublin 2
Phone: 353 1 6772994

#296
**Basic Instincts**
Category: Adult
Average price: Expensive
Area: Temple Bar
Address: 8 Eustace St Dublin 2
Phone: 353 1 6334400

#297
**Sabotage Too**
Category: Women's Clothing
Average price: Expensive
Area: South Inner City
Address: 14 Exchequer St Dublin 2
Phone: 353 1 6778713

#298
**Genius**
Category: Men's Clothing
Average price: Expensive
Area: South Inner City
Address: 6a Powerscourt Townhouse
Centre Dublin 2
Phone: 353 1 6797851

#299
**Alila Boutique**
Category: Women's Clothing, Jewelry
Average price: Expensive
Area: South Inner City
Address: 41 Drury St Dublin 2
Phone: 353 1 6776904

#300
**McCullough Pigott**
Category: Musical Instruments
Average price: Modest
Area: South Inner City
Address: 11 William St S Dublin 2
Phone: 353 1 6773138

#301
**Evolution**
Category: Home & Garden,
Arts & Crafts, Accessories
Average price: Modest
Area: North Inner City
Address: Unit 6 GPO Arcade Dublin 1
Phone: 353 1 8748782

#302
**Banba Toymaster**
Category: Toy Store
Average price: Inexpensive
Area: North Inner City
Address: 48 Mary St Dublin 1
Phone: 353 1 8727100

#303
**Army Bargains**
Category: Outdoor Gear
Area: North Inner City
Address: 29-30 Little Mary St Dublin 1
Phone: 353 1 8744600

#304
**Ruby Ruby**
Category: Luggage, Used,
Vintage, Consignment
Average price: Expensive
Area: South Inner City
Address: Royal Hibernian Way Dublin 2
Phone: 353 1 6725870

#305
**Irish Cancer Society Shop**
Category: Home & Garden
Average price: Inexpensive
Area: Harcourt
Address: Camden St Dublin 2
Phone: 353 1 4750811

#306
**Greene's Florist**
Category: Florist
Average price: Expensive
Area: Monkstown
Address: 103 Monkstown Rd Dublin 1
Phone: 353 1 2805558

#307
**Boots**
Category: Drugstore
Average price: Modest
Area: South Inner City
Address: 12 Grafton St Dublin 2
Phone: 353 1 6773000

#308
**Scribbles Newsagents**
Category: Bookstore
Average price: Inexpensive
Area: Drumcondra
Address: 24 Drumcondra Rd
Upper Dublin 9
Phone: 353 1 8377158

#309
**Crowley Pharmacy**
Category: Drugstore
Average price: Inexpensive
Area: Ballyfermot
Address: 207 Decies Rd Dublin 10
Phone: 353 1 6264528

#310
**Charlestown Shopping Centre**
Category: Shopping Center
Average price: Modest
Area: Ballymun
Address: St. Margarets Rd Dublin 11
Phone: 353 1 8504700

#311
**BT2 Dundrum Town Centre**
Category: Department Store,
Women's Clothing, Men's Clothing
Average price: Expensive
Area: Clonskeagh
Address: Unit 133 Dundrum Town
Centre Dublin 16
Phone: 353 1 2968400

#312
**Book Worms**
Category: Bookstore
Average price: Inexpensive
Area: North Inner City
Address: 75 Middle Abbey St Dublin 1
Phone: 353 1 8735772

#313
**Vincent's**
Category: Thrift Store
Area: Rathmines
Address: 310 Lower Rathmines Rd Dublin 6
Phone: 353 1 4973409

#314
**The Loop**
Category: Cosmetics & Beauty
Average price: Modest
Area: Santry
Address: Arrivals Hall Dublin
Phone: 353 1 800747747

#315
**Waltons New School of Music**
Category: Musical Instruments,
Specialty School
Average price: Expensive
Area: South Inner City
Address: 69 South Great George's St
Dublin 2
Phone: 353 1 4781884

#316
**Brooks & Co.**
Category: Antiques
Average price: Expensive
Area: South Inner City
Address: 136 Lower Baggot St Dublin 4
Phone: 353 1 6789845

#317
**Temple Bar Trading Company**
Category: Personal Shopping
Average price: Expensive
Area: Temple Bar
Address: 43 Temple Bar Dublin 2
Phone: 353 1 67252867

#318
**River Island**
Category: Men's Clothing,
Women's Clothing, Accessories
Average price: Modest
Area: South Inner City
Address: 103 Grafton St Dublin 2
Phone: 353 1 6778251

#319
**Clarks**
Category: Shoe Store
Average price: Modest
Area: North Inner City
Address: Henry St Dublin 1
Phone: 353 1 8721384

#320
**Korky's**
Category: Shoe Store
Average price: Modest
Area: North Inner City
Address: 4 GPO Buildings
Henry St Dublin 2
Phone: 353 1 8731359

#321
**Industry**
Category: Concept Shop
Area: North Inner City
Address: 5 Essex St West,
Bottom of Cow's lane Dublin 8
Phone: 353 1 6139111

#322
**Fields Jewellers**
Category: Jewelry
Average price: Expensive
Area: North Inner City
Address: 1a Jervis Centre Dublin 1
Phone: 353 1 8781578

#323
### Samia's
**Category:** Shoe Store, Accessories
**Average price:** Modest
**Area:** North Inner City
**Address:** 9 Mary St Dublin 1
**Phone:** 353 1 8735945

#324
### WM Trimmings
**Category:** Fabric Store, Knitting Supplies
**Average price:** Modest
**Area:** North Inner City
**Address:** 137 Capel St Dublin 1
**Phone:** 353 1 8280301

#325
### Carrolls Irish Gifts
**Category:** Toy Store, Souvenir Shop
**Average price:** Inexpensive
**Area:** South Inner City
**Address:** 22 Suffolk St Dublin 2
**Phone:** 353 1 6337699

#326
### Dixon Hempenstall Opticians
**Category:** Eyewear & Opticians
**Average price:** Expensive
**Area:** South Inner City
**Address:** 14 Suffolk St Dublin 2
**Phone:** 353 1 6771334

#327
### Evans
**Category:** Women's Clothing
**Average price:** Expensive
**Area:** South Inner City
**Address:** Liffey Valley SC Quarryvale
Dublin 20
**Phone:** 353 1 6234728

#328
### Raidar
**Category:** Men's Clothing
**Average price:** Expensive
**Area:** South Inner City
**Address:** Unit 106 Dublin 2
**Phone:** 353 1 4783221

#329
### O Neills Shoes
**Category:** Shoe Store
**Area:** North Inner City
**Address:** 11 Talbot St Dublin 1
**Phone:** 353 1 8745348

#330
### JoJo Mama Bebe
**Category:** Maternity Wear
**Area:** South Inner City
**Address:** 14 Wicklow St Dublin 2
**Phone:** 353 1 6336805

#331
### Birkenstock
**Category:** Shoe Store
**Area:** South Inner City
**Address:** 36 Wicklow St Dublin 2
**Phone:** 353 1 6753766

#332
### Heatons Ltd
**Category:** Department Store
**Average price:** Exclusive
**Area:** South Inner City
**Address:** Heaton House, IDA
Business Park Dublin 24
**Phone:** 353 1 4630100

#333
### The Douglas Hyde Gallery
**Category:** Art Gallery
**Average price:** Inexpensive
**Area:** South Inner City
**Address:** Trinity College Dublin 2
**Phone:** 353 1 8961116

#334
### Sally
**Category:** Cosmetics & Beauty
**Average price:** Modest
**Area:** South Inner City
**Address:** 21 Drury St Dublin
**Phone:** 353 1 6774904

#335
### Project 51
**Category:** Accessories, Jewelry
**Area:** South Inner City
**Address:** 51 S William St Dublin 2
**Phone:** 353 1 6795551

#336
### Gallery Number One
**Category:** Art Gallery
**Average price:** Expensive
**Area:** South Inner City
**Address:** 1 Castle St Dublin 2
**Phone:** 353 1 4789090

#337
**The Green Gallery**
**Category:** Art Gallery
**Area:** South Inner City
**Address:** St Stephens Green Center
**Phone:** 353 85 1988441

#338
**Patrick St. Pharmacy**
**Category:** Drugstore
**Area:** The Liberties
**Address:** Ardilaun Court Dublin 8
**Phone:** 353 1 4544897

#339
**Adonis Flower Designers**
**Category:** Home & Garden
**Average price:** Modest
**Area:** Clanbrassil St
**Address:** 59-60 Patrick St Dublin 8
**Phone:** 353 1 4545973

#340
**Henry Jermyn**
**Category:** Men's Clothing, Accessories
**Average price:** Modest
**Area:** South Inner City
**Address:** 16 Clare St Dublin 2
**Phone:** 353 1 6760500

#341
**Portfolio on Francis St.**
**Category:** Art Gallery
**Area:** The Liberties
**Address:** 67-68 Francis St Dublin 8
**Phone:** 353 1 4537124

#342
**Royal Hibernian Academy**
**Category:** Museum, Art Gallery
**Area:** South Inner City
**Address:** 15 Ely Place Dublin 2
**Phone:** 353 1 6612558

#343
**Freewheeling**
**Category:** Bikes, Bike Repair/Maintenance
**Average price:** Modest
**Area:** Grand Canal Dock
**Address:** 96 Pearse St Dublin 2
**Phone:** 353 1 6773111

#344
**Phibsboro Hardware**
**Category:** Hardware Store
**Average price:** Modest
**Area:** Phibsboro
**Address:** 109 Phibsboro Rd Dublin 7
**Phone:** 353 1 8301267

#345
**My Beer and Wine**
**Category:** Beer, Wine, Spirits,
Hobby Shop
**Area:** Rathmines
**Address:** 92 Lower Rathmines Rd Dublin 6
**Phone:** 353 1 4977231

#346
**Doc Morris**
**Category:** Drugstore
**Average price:** Modest
**Area:** Rathmines
**Address:** 282 Lower Rathmines Rd Dublin 6
**Phone:** 353 1 4970750

#347
**Ranelagh Cycles**
**Category:** Bikes
**Average price:** Inexpensive
**Area:** Rathgar
**Address:** 7 Ranelagh Village Dublin 6
**Phone:** 353 1 4960300

#348
**Miss Selfridge**
**Category:** Women's Clothing
**Average price:** Expensive
**Area:** Ringsend
**Address:** Level 3 19 The Square Dublin
**Phone:** 353 1 8722206

#349
**Bookcube Gallery & Bookshop**
**Category:** Art Gallery, Books,
Mags, Music & Video
**Area:** Rathmines
**Address:** 203 Lower Rathmines Rd Dublin 6
**Phone:** 353 1 4961064

#350
**Morehampton Pharmacy**
**Category:** Drugstore
**Average price:** Modest
**Area:** Milltown
**Address:** 79 Morehampton Rd Dublin 4
**Phone:** 353 1 6687103

#351
**Rosalins**
**Category:** Bookstore, Gift Shop
**Average price:** Inexpensive
**Area:** Rathgar
**Address:** 42 Dunville Avenue Dublin 6
**Phone:** 353 1 4972330

#352
**Harolds Bazaar**
**Category:** Antiques
**Average price:** Inexpensive
**Area:** Harold's Cross
**Address:** Harolds Cross Rd Dublin 6w
**Phone:** 353 87 7228789

#353
**Hickey's Pharmacy**
**Category:** Drugstore
**Average price:** Inexpensive
**Area:** Harold's Cross
**Address:** 310 Harold's Cross Rd
Dublin 6w
**Phone:** 353 1 4923977

#354
**Sandymount Pharmacy**
**Category:** Drugstore
**Average price:** Expensive
**Area:** Irishtown
**Address:** 1a Sandymount Green
Dublin 4
**Phone:** 353 1 2837188

#355
**AffinityD6**
**Category:** Home & Garden,
Flowers & Gifts
**Area:** Terenure
**Address:** 14 Orwell Rd Dublin 6
**Phone:** 353 1 4970222

#356
**Mick Dowling Sportsworld**
**Category:** Sports Wear
**Area:** Terenure
**Address:** 66 Terenure Rd N Dublin 6
**Phone:** 353 1 4904502

#357
**Mccabes Pharmacy**
**Category:** Drugstore
**Average price:** Modest
**Area:** Clonskeagh
**Address:** Dundrum Town Centre
Dublin 16
**Phone:** 353 1 2961100

#358
**Crescendo Music**
**Category:** Musical Instruments
**Area:** Windy Arbour
**Address:** 86-88 Terenure Rd
N Dublin 6w
**Phone:** 353 1 4929998

#359
**The Flower Box**
**Category:** Florist
**Average price:** Modest
**Area:** Mount Merrion
**Address:** 31 The Rise Dublin 4
**Phone:** 353 1 6609470

#360
**McKenna Man**
**Category:** Men's Clothing
**Area:** Rathfarnham
**Address:** 20 Nutgrove Shopping
Centre Dublin 14
**Phone:** 353 1 4933066

#361
**Irene's Flower Cabin**
**Category:** Florist
**Area:** Dundrum
**Address:** 13A Main St Dublin 14
**Phone:** 353 1 2960200

#362
**The Health Store**
**Category:** Shopping
**Average price:** Modest
**Area:** Mount Merrion
**Address:** Frascati Centre Dublin
**Phone:** 353 1 2788855

#363
**Terrisales**
**Category:** Cosmetics & Beauty
**Area:** North Inner City
**Address:** 71 Middle Abbey St Dublin 1
**Phone:** 353 1 8724700

#364
**Simon Hart**
**Category:** Shoe Store
**Area:** North Inner City
**Address:** 40 Henry St Dublin 1
**Phone:** 353 1 8726376

#365
**O2 Store**
**Category:** Electronics
**Area:** North Inner City
**Address:** 5 Henry Stree Dublin 1
**Phone:** 353 1 8779000

#366
**UNICEF Ireland**
**Category:** Thrift Store
**Area:** North Inner City
**Address:** 33 Lower Ormond Quay
**Phone:** 353 1 8783000

#367
**Fields**
**Category:** Jewelry
**Average price:** Expensive
**Area:** North Inner City
**Address:** 30 Henry St Dublin 1
**Phone:** 353 1 8723099

#368
**Skechers**
**Category:** Shoe Store
**Area:** North Inner City
**Address:** 4 Henry St Dublin 1
**Phone:** 353 1 8730055

#369
**D8 Fitness**
**Category:** Gyms, Fitness, Equipment
**Area:** North Inner City
**Address:** 12 Lower 12 Bridge St
**Phone:** 353 1 4735847

#370
**Grant Templebar Opticians**
**Category:** Eyewear & Opticians
**Average price:** Modest
**Area:** Temple Bar
**Address:** 41 Wellington QuayDublin 2
**Phone:** 353 1 6775982

#371
**Love Furniture**
**Category:** Furniture Store
**Average price:** Inexpensive
**Area:** North Inner City
**Address:** Ballymount House, Parkway
Business Centre Dublin
**Phone:** 353 1 9022711

#372
**O'connor R**
**Category:** Jewelry
**Area:** North Inner City
**Address:** 32 Lower O'Connell St Dublin 1
**Phone:** 353 1 8740701

#373
**Old World New**
**Category:** Hobby Shop, Antiques
**Average price:** Modest
**Area:** Temple Bar
**Address:** 12 Crown Alley Dublin 2
**Phone:** 353 87 1903282

#374
**Photo Care**
**Category:** Photography Store
**Area:** North Inner City
**Address:** 31 Abbey St Lower Dublin 1
**Phone:** 353 1 8786669

#375
**McDowell & Co.**
**Category:** Jewelry
**Area:** North Inner City
**Address:** 3 Upper O'Connell St Dublin 1
**Phone:** 353 1 8743184

#376
**Penneys**
**Category:** Department Store
**Average price:** Inexpensive
**Area:** North Inner City
**Address:** 47 Mary St Dublin 1
**Phone:** 353 86 2551106

#377
**Treacy's Pharmacy**
**Category:** Drugstore
**Area:** North Inner City
**Address:** Eden Quay Dublin 1
**Phone:** 353 1 8740179

#378
**Argos**
**Category:** Department Store
**Area:** North Inner City
**Address:** 23 Mary St Dublin 1
**Phone:** 353 1 8722821

#379
**Mc'Neills Music Shop**
**Category:** Musical Instruments
**Average price:** Inexpensive
**Area:** North Inner City
**Address:** 140 Capel St Dublin 1
**Phone:** 353 1 8728530

#380
**Hall Cameras**
**Category:** Photography Store
**Area:** North Inner City
**Address:** 95 Talbot St Dublin 1
**Phone:** 353 1 8788332

#381
**Flagship Scubadiving**
**Category:** Scuba Diving
**Area:** South Inner City
**Address:** Grand Canal Baslin
Ringsend Dublin 4
**Phone:** 353 1 6670988

#382
**IBM Ireland**
Category: Shopping
Area: South Inner City
Address: 1 George Dock's Dublin
Phone: 353 86 8544189

#383
**The Gadget Shop**
Category: Department Store
Area: South Inner City
Address: Unit 7 Old Bawn Shopping
Centre Dublin 1
Phone: 353 1 8783887

#384
**Smyths Toys**
Category: Sporting Goods
Area: South Inner City
Address: Fonthill Retail Park
Fonthill Rd Dublin 22
Phone: 353 1 6304450

#385
**Belle Cheminee**
Category: Furniture Store
Average price: Expensive
Area: Parnell Square
Address: 106 Capel St Dublin 1
Phone: 353 1 8724122

#386
**A-Wear**
Category: Fashion
Average price: Modest
Area: South Inner City
Address: Northside Dublin 17
Phone: 353 1 8477583

#387
**Cherriebum**
Category: Women's Clothing
Average price: Modest
Area: South Inner City
Address: 30 Exchequer St Dublin 2
Phone: 353 1 6727788

#388
**Burtons**
Category: Men's Clothing
Area: South Inner City
Address: U 202 Blanchardstown Town
Centre Dublin 15
Phone: 353 1 8221849

#389
**Cath Kidston**
Category: Women's Clothing, Gift Shop
Average price: Modest
Area: South Inner City
Address: 104 Grafton St Dublin
Phone: 353 1 6753618

#390
**Clyne Gallery**
Category: Art Gallery
Area: South Inner City
Address: Exchange St Upper Dublin 2
Phone: 353 1 6770107

#391
**Watt Bros**
Category: Home & Garden
Area: Four Courts
Address: 18 Ormond Quay
Upper Dublin 7
Phone: 353 1 6778574

#392
**MAC Cosmetics**
Category: Makeup Artist,
Cosmetics & Beauty
Average price: Modest
Area: South Inner City
Address: 92 Grafton St Dublin 2
Phone: 353 1 6056666

#393
**Bygone Days**
Category: Antiques
Average price: Modest
Area: South Inner City
Address: Market Arcade South Great
Georges St Dublin 2
Phone: 353 86 3210740

#394
**Debbie Paul Studio & Gallery**
Category: Art Gallery
Area: Temple Bar
Address: 1 Cows Lane Dublin 8
Phone: 353 1 6751814

#395
**Beaux Bows**
Category: Vintage, Consignment,
Women's Clothing
Average price: Modest
Area: South Inner City
Address: 21/22 Georges St Arcade
Dublin 2
Phone: 353 1 7991940

#396
**Perk Up Vintage**
**Category:** Vintage
**Area:** South Inner City
**Address:** 59 South William St Dublin 2
**Phone:** 353 87 0555326

#397
**Tiffany & Co.**
**Category:** Watches, Jewelry
**Average price:** Expensive
**Area:** South Inner City
**Address:** 88-95 Grafton St Dublin 2
**Phone:** 353 1 6056722

#398
**Dublin Picture Framing**
**Category:** Framing
**Average price:** Expensive
**Area:** South Inner City
**Address:** 15 Southwilliam St Dublin
**Phone:** 353 86 2013530

#399
**Kennedy & McSharry**
**Category:** Men's Clothing, Accessories
**Area:** South Inner City
**Address:** South William St Dublin 2
**Phone:** 353 1 6778770

#400
**Tower Records**
**Category:** Books, Mags, Music & Video
**Average price:** Modest
**Area:** South Inner City
**Address:** 7 Dawson St Dublin 2
**Phone:** 353 1 6713250

#401
**De Búrca Rare Books**
**Category:** Bookstore, Antiques
**Area:** South Inner City
**Address:** 51a Dawson St Dublin 2
**Phone:** 353 1 6719609

#402
**Patrick Donald**
**Photography Gallery**
**Category:** Art Gallery
**Area:** South Inner City
**Address:** 8/9 Royal Hiberian Way
**Phone:** 353 1 6815225

#403
**Ciara Bridal**
**Category:** Bridal
**Average price:** Modest
**Area:** South Inner City
**Address:** Powerscourt Shopping Centre
**Phone:** 353 1 6711546

#404
**Goldfinger**
**Category:** Jewelry
**Area:** South Inner City
**Address:** 14 S Anne St Dublin 2
**Phone:** 353 1 6714203

#405
**Maurice Abrahams**
**Category:** Fashion
**Average price:** Expensive
**Area:** South Inner City
**Address:** 17a South Annes St Dublin 2
**Phone:** 353 1 6770167

#406
**Wicked Frills**
**Category:** Fashion
**Area:** Inns Quay
**Address:** 82 Dorset St Dublin
**Phone:** 353 1 8603062

#407
**The Goddess Room**
**Category:** Women's Clothing
**Area:** South Inner City
**Address:** Grafton St Dublin
**Phone:** 353 83 4187970

#408
**Danker Antiques**
**Category:** Antiques, Jewelry
**Area:** South Inner City
**Address:** 4 - 5 Royal Hibernian
Way Dublin 2
**Phone:** 353 1 6774009

#409
**MRCB Paints**
**Category:** Home Decor
**Area:** Thomas St
**Address:** 12-13 Cornmarket Dublin 8
**Phone:** 353 1 6798755

#410
**Reilly's Pharmacy Thomas St.**
**Category:** Drugstore
**Average price:** Modest
**Area:** The Liberties
**Address:** Thomas St Dublin 8
**Phone:** 353 1 4548198

#411
**St Kevins Mart**
**Category:** Bookstore
**Average price:** Inexpensive
**Area:** Clanbrassil St
**Address:** 14a Upper Kevin St Dublin 8
**Phone:** 353 1 4535293

#412
**Voltaire Diamonds**
**Category:** Jewelry
**Area:** Harcourt
**Address:** 15 Harcourt St Dublin 2
**Phone:** 353 1 4794220

#413
**Houseworks**
**Category:** Furniture Store, Home Decor, Kitchen & Bath
**Average price:** Exclusive
**Area:** Grand Canal Dock
**Address:** 11-15 Upper Erne St Dublin 2
**Phone:** 353 1 6769511

#414
**Manor D.I.Y**
**Category:** Hardware Store
**Area:** Stoneybatter
**Address:** Unit 3, Norseman Court Dublin 7
**Phone:** 353 67 29220

#415
**Douglas Interiors**
**Category:** Home Decor
**Average price:** Modest
**Area:** Harcourt
**Address:** 32 Lower Camden St Dublin 2
**Phone:** 353 1 4752951

#416
**Frame F X**
**Category:** Framing
**Area:** BRdstone
**Address:** 177 Phibsborough Rd Dublin 7
**Phone:** 353 1 8601414

#417
**Cahills Pharmacy**
**Category:** Drugstore
**Average price:** Modest
**Area:** Harcourt
**Address:** Lower Camden St Dublin 2
**Phone:** 353 1 4753160

#418
**Jon Jon Museum**
**Category:** Art Gallery
**Average price:** Inexpensive
**Area:** Grand Canal Dock
**Address:** Asgard Rd Dublin
**Phone:** 353 89 2191933

#419
**Thomas Carroll Opticians**
**Category:** Eyewear & Opticians
**Area:** Baggot St
**Address:** 3 Pembroke Terrace Dublin
**Phone:** 353 1 2986643

#420
**Cup Cakes Lingerie**
**Category:** Lingerie
**Area:** Rathgar
**Address:** 44-46 Ranelagh Village Dublin 6
**Phone:** 353 1 4126876

#421
**Phoenix Framers**
**Category:** Framing
**Area:** Ringsend
**Address:** 16A St. Brendan's Cottages Dublin 4
**Phone:** 353 1 6674318

#422
**The Portrait Studio**
**Category:** Photographers, Photography Store
**Area:** Clontarf
**Address:** 62 Clontarf Rd Dublin 3
**Phone:** 353 1 8186630

#423
**Foleys of Clontarf Pharmacy**
**Category:** Drugstore
**Area:** Clontarf
**Address:** 63 Clontarf Rd Dublin 3
**Phone:** 353 1 8336384

#424
**AC Boles**
**Category:** Drugstore
**Area:** Island Bridge
**Address:** Emmet Rd Dublin 8
**Phone:** 353 1 4534291

#425
**Best Buds**
**Category:** Home & Garden
**Area:** Clontarf
**Address:** 187 Howth Rd Dublin 5
**Phone:** 353 1 8535439

#426
**Perfect Ring**
**Category:** Jewelry
**Area:** Clontarf
**Address:** Vernon Avenue Dublin
**Phone:** 353 1 4422472

#427
**Clontarf Florist**
**Category:** Florist
**Average price:** Modest
**Area:** Clontarf
**Address:** St Gabriels Rd Dublin 3
**Phone:** 353 1 8531441

#428
**A-Z Hire**
**Category:** Hardware Store,
Building Supplies
**Area:** Walkinstown
**Address:** 15 Walkinstown Green
Dublin 12
**Phone:** 353 1 4192800

#429
**Magpie's Nest Antique, Vintage & Modern Jewellery**
**Category:** Antiques, Jewelry
**Average price:** Modest
**Area:** Crumlin
**Address:** 178A Whitehall Rd W Dublin 12
**Phone:** 353 1 4553355

#430
**Counter Propaganda**
**Category:** Men's Clothing
**Area:** Walkinstown
**Address:** Stephen's Green Shopping
Centre Dublin 2
**Phone:** 353 1 4251115

#431
**Inglot**
**Category:** Cosmetics & Beauty,
Makeup Artist
**Average price:** Modest
**Area:** Dundrum
**Address:** Dundrum Town Centre
Dublin 16
**Phone:** 353 1 2981909

#432
**Bhagwan Pharmacy**
**Category:** Drugstore
**Average price:** Modest
**Area:** Dundrum
**Address:** Ballinteer Rd Dublin 16
**Phone:** 353 1 2984378

#433
**The Collectors' Shop**
**Category:** Antiques
**Area:** Blackrock
**Address:** Blackrock Market Dublin
**Phone:** 353 87 9252746

#434
**Coolmine Décor**
**Category:** Home Decor
**Area:** Blanchardstown
**Address:** Clonsilla Rd Dublin 15
**Phone:** 353 1 8209566

#435
**Accessorize**
**Category:** Women's Clothing
**Area:** Blanchardstown
**Address:** Blanchardstown Centre Dublin 15
**Phone:** 353 1 8222228

#436
**Elverys Intersport**
**Category:** Sporting Goods
**Area:** Blanchardstown
**Address:** Unit 4 12 Blanchardstown Retail
Park Dublin 15
**Phone:** 353 1 8211939

#437
**Sheanes Pharmacy**
**Category:** Drugstore
**Area:** Foxrock
**Address:** 92 Foxrock Avenue Dublin 18
**Phone:** 353 1 2893085

#438
**Paul Sexton**
**Category:** Home & Garden
**Area:** Foxrock
**Address:** Cornelscourt Dublin 18
**Phone:** 353 1 2896396

#439
**Rorys Fishing Tackle**
**Category:** Outdoor Gear
**Average price:** Modest
**Area:** Temple Bar
**Address:** 17a Temple Bar Dublin 2
**Phone:** 353 1 6772351

#440
**Argos**
**Category:** Department Store
**Average price:** Modest
**Area:** North Inner City
**Address:** Henry St Dublin 1
**Phone:** 353 1 8725100

#441
**Wallis Fashion Group**
**Category:** Women's Clothing
**Average price:** Modest
**Area:** South Inner City
**Address:** 104 Grafton St Dublin 2
**Phone:** 353 1 6798349

#442
**Costelloe & Costelloe**
**Category:** Accessories, Luggage
**Average price:** Modest
**Area:** South Inner City
**Address:** 14a Chatham St Dublin 2
**Phone:** 353 1 6714209

#443
**Onboard**
**Category:** Sports Wear
**Average price:** Expensive
**Area:** South Inner City
**Address:** Creation Arcade Dublin 2
**Phone:** 353 1 6728767

#444
**Tiger Lily**
**Category:** Flowers & Gifts
**Average price:** Modest
**Area:** Cork St
**Address:** Dublin 8
**Phone:** 353 1 4758564

#445
**Gloss Hair & Beauty Salon**
**Category:** Hair Salon,
Cosmetics & Beauty
**Average price:** Modest
**Area:** Harcourt
**Address:** 42 S Richmond St Dublin 2
**Phone:** 353 1 4758798

#446
**Meagher's Pharmacy**
**Category:** Drugstore
**Average price:** Modest
**Area:** Baggot St
**Address:** 10 Upper Baggot St Dublin 4
**Phone:** 353 1 6605744

#447
**Unique Flowers & Interior**
**Category:** Flowers & Gifts
**Average price:** Modest
**Area:** Dalkey
**Address:** 42 Castle St Dublin
**Phone:** 353 1 2751737

#448
**Superquinn**
**Category:** Grocery, Cosmetics & Beauty,
Newspapers & Magazines
**Average price:** Modest
**Area:** Rathgar
**Address:** 31-33 Ranelagh Dublin 6
**Phone:** 353 1 4964270

#449
**Vincent's**
**Category:** Thrift Store
**Average price:** Inexpensive
**Area:** South Inner City
**Address:** 3 Whitefriars Unit Dublin 2
**Phone:** 353 1 4789672

#450
**Vision Express**
**Category:** Eyewear & Opticians
**Average price:** Modest
**Area:** Blanchardstown
**Address:** Unit 118 Dublin 15
**Phone:** 353 1 8222066

#451
**Duff Cycles**
**Category:** Bikes
**Average price:** Modest
**Area:** Clongriffin
**Address:** Unit 12 Dublin 13
**Phone:** 353 1 8671151

#452
**KHO**
**Category:** Luggage
**Average price:** Modest
**Area:** South Inner City
**Address:** 11 Lord Edward St Dublin 2
**Phone:** 353 1 6790665

#453
**Homebase Ireland**
**Category:** Hardware Store
**Average price:** Modest
**Area:** Rathfarnham
**Address:** Nutgrove Avenue Dublin 14
**Phone:** 353 1 2983644

#454
**Music Minds**
**Category:** Music & DVDs
**Average price:** Modest
**Area:** North Inner City
**Address:** 33 Lower Liffey St Dublin 1
**Phone:** 353 1 8720233

#455
**Zerep**
**Category:** Shoe Store
**Average price:** Modest
**Area:** North Inner City
**Address:** 12 Upper Liffey St Dublin 12
**Phone:** 353 1 8746536

#456
**Vodafone Retail**
**Category:** Mobile Phones
**Area:** North Inner City
**Address:** 51 Henry St Dublin 1
**Phone:** 353 1 8735020

#457
**Cleary's Pharmacy**
**Category:** Drugstore
**Area:** North Inner City
**Address:** 6 Talbot St Dublin 1
**Phone:** 353 1 8786935

#458
**K2 Camping & Clothing**
**Category:** Outdoor Gear
**Average price:** Inexpensive
**Area:** North Inner City
**Address:** 101 Talbot St Dublin 1
**Phone:** 353 1 8741717

#459
**Michael Guineys**
**Category:** Department Store
**Average price:** Inexpensive
**Area:** North Inner City
**Address:** 93 Talbot St Dublin 1
**Phone:** 353 1 8726788

#460
**P & P Barry**
**Category:** Tobacco Shop,
Convenience Store
**Average price:** Inexpensive
**Area:** South Inner City
**Address:** 30 King St Dublin 2
**Phone:** 353 1 6773462

#461
**Oasis**
**Category:** Women's Clothing, Accessories
**Average price:** Modest
**Area:** South Inner City
**Address:** 3 St Stephen's Green Dublin 2
**Phone:** 353 1 6714477

#462
**Scarecrow Flowers**
**Category:** Florist, Party Supplies,
Wedding Planning
**Average price:** Expensive
**Area:** Irishtown
**Address:** 95a Sandymount Rd Dublin 4
**Phone:** 353 1 6681189

#463
**Nutley Newsagents**
**Category:** Newspapers & Magazines
**Average price:** Modest
**Area:** Merrion
**Address:** 85 Merrion Rd Dublin 4
**Phone:** 353 1 2838122

#464
**Mango**
**Category:** Women's Clothing
**Area:** Lucan
**Address:** Complex 22 Dublin 22
**Phone:** 353 1 6239078

#465
**Blacktie**
**Category:** Men's Clothing
**Area:** South Inner City
**Address:** 140 Lower Baggot St Dublin 1
**Phone:** 353 1 6763128

#466
**Jamestown Market**
**Category:** Shopping
**Area:** Inchicore
**Address:** 90 Jamestown Rd Dublin 8
**Phone:** 353 86 8253370

#467
**Enable Ireland**
**Category:** Community Service,
Vintage, Consignment
**Area:** The Liberties
**Address:** 69 Thomas St Dublin 8
**Phone:** 353 1 4542681

#468
**Walton's World of Music**
**Category:** Musical Instruments
**Average price:** Expensive
**Area:** South Inner City
**Address:** 59-70 S Great
Georges St Dublin 2
**Phone:** 353 1 4750661

#469
**Mojo's Records**
**Category:** Vinyl Records
**Area:** Temple Bar
**Address:** 4 Merchant's Arch Dublin 2
**Phone:** 353 1 6727905

#470
**Jack & Jones**
**Category:** Men's Clothing
**Average price:** Modest
**Area:** South Inner City
**Address:** 6-9 Trinity St Dublin 2
**Phone:** 353 1 6707387

#471
**A Store is Born**
**Category:** Vintage, Consignment
**Average price:** Modest
**Area:** South Inner City
**Address:** 34 Clarendon St Dublin 2
**Phone:** 353 1 2857627

#472
**Grant's**
**Category:** Photographers,
Photography Store
**Area:** Baggot St
**Address:** 33 Upper Baggot St Dublin 4
**Phone:** 353 1 6604288

#473
**NoName**
**Category:** Women's Clothing, Accessories
**Average price:** Modest
**Area:** North Inner City
**Address:** 38 Henry St Dublin 1
**Phone:** 353 1 8730953

#474
**Dunnes Store**
**Category:** Department Store
**Average price:** Modest
**Area:** South Inner City
**Address:** 62 Grafton St Dublin 1
**Phone:** 353 1 6714629

#475
**Murphys**
**Category:** Bookstore
**Average price:** Inexpensive
**Area:** South Inner City
**Address:** 146 Lower Baggot St Dublin 2
**Phone:** 353 1 6762042

#476
**Dundrum Center**
**Category:** Shopping Center
**Average price:** Modest
**Area:** Milltown
**Address:** Sandyford Rd Dublin
**Phone:** 353 1 2991700

#477
**The Sweetest Things Gift Shop**
**Category:** Flowers & Gifts
**Area:** Harold's Cross
**Address:** Sundrive Rd Dublin 12
**Phone:** 353 1 4063800

#478
**Mrs Quins Charity Shop**
**Category:** Shopping
**Area:** Inchicore
**Address:** 9B Gratten Crescent Dublin
**Phone:** 353 87 1394330

#479
**Petstop Superstore**
**Category:** Home & Garden
**Average price:** Expensive
**Area:** Beaumont
**Address:** 2B West End Retail Park Dublin 15
**Phone:** 353 1 2941336

#480
**GAA Ticket Shop**
**Category:** Shopping
**Average price:** Inexpensive
**Area:** Ballybough
**Address:** 53A Dorset St Dublin
**Phone:** 353 1 8363222

#481
**Bridal Outlet**
**Category:** Women's Clothing, Bridal
**Average price:** Modest
**Area:** Baldoyle
**Address:** Unit 9 Abbey Bus Park Dublin 13
**Phone:** 353 1 8395358

#482
**Tesco**
**Category:** Grocery
**Average price:** Modest
**Area:** Rathgar
**Address:** Upper Rathmines Rd Dublin 6
**Phone:** 353 1 4970611

#483
**O2 Store**
**Category:** Mobile Phones
**Average price:** Expensive
**Area:** Baggot St
**Address:** 3A Upper Baggot St Dublin 2
**Phone:** 353 1 6643530

#484
**Nourish**
**Category:** Health Market,
Cosmetics & Beauty
**Area:** Rathfarnham
**Address:** Unit 36 Nutgrove Shopping
Centre Dublin 14
**Phone:** 353 1 4935289

#485
**The 3rd Policeman**
**Category:** Antiques, Vintage
**Average price:** Modest
**Area:** Rathmines
**Address:** 121 Lower Rathmines Rd Dublin 6
**Phone:** 353 1 5550002

#486
**Maplin Electronics**
**Category:** Electronics
**Average price:** Expensive
**Area:** Blanchardstown
**Address:** 413 Blanchardstown T
Ctr Dublin 15
**Phone:** 353 1 8215810

#487
**Fresh**
**Category:** Women's Clothing,
Men's Clothing, Vintage
**Average price:** Modest
**Area:** Temple Bar
**Address:** 1 Crown Alley Dublin 2
**Phone:** 353 1 6718423

#488
**Skate City**
**Category:** Sporting Goods
**Average price:** Exclusive
**Area:** Temple Bar
**Address:** 14 Crown Alley Dublin 2
**Phone:** 353 1 6799900

#489
**Angel Cruisers**
**Category:** Bike Rentals, Bikes
**Average price:** Modest
**Area:** North Inner City
**Address:** 5 Great Strand St Dublin 1
**Phone:** 353 85 7278901

#490
**Cash Converters**
**Category:** Pawn Shop
**Area:** North Inner City
**Address:** Parnell St Mall Dublin 1
**Phone:** 353 1 8727070

#491
**Moi & Toi**
**Category:** Women's Clothing
**Area:** North Inner City
**Address:** 105-106 Talbot St Dublin 1
**Phone:** 353 1 8746270

#492
**Hackett's Garden Shop**
**Category:** Nursery, Gardening
**Average price:** Inexpensive
**Area:** North Inner City
**Address:** 4 Capel St Dublin 1
**Phone:** 353 1 8734911

#493
**Indigo & Cloth**
**Category:** Men's Clothing, Print Media
**Average price:** Expensive
**Address:** No.9 Essex St East Dublin 2
**Phone:** 353 1 6706403

#494
**McCullough Piggot's**
**Category:** Musical Instruments
**Area:** South Inner City
**Address:** 11 S William St Dublin 2
**Phone:** 353 1 6773138

#495
**Murphy Sheehy & Co.**
**Category:** Fabric Store
**Area:** South Inner City
**Address:** 14 Castle Market Dublin 2
**Phone:** 353 1 6770316

#496
**R & C McCormack**
**Category:** Jewelry
**Area:** South Inner City
**Address:** 51 Grafton St Dublin 2
**Phone:** 353 1 6773737

#497
**Mad Hatter**
**Category:** Accessories
**Average price:** Expensive
**Area:** South Inner City
**Address:** 20 Lower Stephen St Dublin 2
**Phone:** 353 1 4054936

#498
**Nu Essence Beauty Salon**
**Category:** Beauty Salon
**Average price:** Modest
**Area:** South Inner City
**Address:** 27 S Anne St Dublin 2
**Phone:** 353 1 6716443

#499
**Dame St. Pharmacy**
**Average price:** Modest
**Area:** South Inner City
**Address:** Dame St Dublin 2
**Phone:** 353 1 6704523

#500
**Coast**
**Category:** Women's Clothing
**Average price:** Expensive
**Area:** South Inner City
**Address:** 5 St Stephens Green
**Phone:** 353 1 6770207

# TOP 500 RESTAURANTS

The Most Recommended by Locals & Trevelers

(From #1 to #500)

#1
**The Butcher Grill**
**Cuisines:** Steakhouse
**Average price:** Expensive
**Area:** Rathgar
**Address:** 92 Ranelagh Village Dublin 6
**Phone:** 353 1 4981805

#2
**Gallagher's Boxty House**
**Cuisines:** Irish
**Average price:** Modest
**Area:** Temple Bar
**Address:** 20/21 Temple Bar Dublin 2
**Phone:** 353 1 6772762

#3
**The Pig's Ear**
**Cuisines:** Bistro, European
**Average price:** Expensive
**Area:** South Inner City
**Address:** 4 Nassau St Dublin 2
**Phone:** 353 1 6703865

#4
**Paulie's Pizza**
**Cuisines:** Pizza
**Average price:** Modest
**Area:** Beggars Bush
**Address:** 58 Grand Canal St Dublin 4
**Phone:** 353 1 6643658

#5
**Queen of Tarts**
**Cuisines:** Desserts, Tea Room,
Breakfast & Brunch
**Average price:** Modest
**Area:** South Inner City
**Address:** Dame St Dublin 2
**Phone:** 353 1 6707499

#6
**Third Space**
**Cuisines:** Irish
**Average price:** Inexpensive
**Area:** Smithfield
**Address:** 14 Smithfield Market Dublin 7
**Phone:** 353 1 5297208

#7
**Cornucopia**
**Cuisines:** Vegetarian
**Average price:** Modest
**Area:** South Inner City
**Address:** 19/20 Wicklow St Dublin 2
**Phone:** 353 1 6777583

#8
**L Mulligan Grocer**
**Cuisines:** Pub, Irish
**Average price:** Modest
**Area:** Stoneybatter
**Address:** 18 Stoneybatter Dublin 7
**Phone:** 353 1 6709889

#9
**Green Nineteen**
**Cuisines:** Gastropub, Irish, Cafe
**Average price:** Modest
**Area:** Harcourt
**Address:** 19 Camden St Lower Dublin 2
**Phone:** 353 1 4789626

#10
**Juniors**
**Cuisines:** Brasserie, European
**Average price:** Modest
**Area:** Beggars Bush
**Address:** 2 Bath Avenue Dublin 4
**Phone:** 353 1 6643648

#11
**The Kitchen**
**Cuisines:** Mediterranean, Irish
**Average price:** Modest
**Area:** South Inner City
**Address:** 3 S Anne St Dublin 2
**Phone:** 353 1 6774205

#12
**The Brazen Head**
**Cuisines:** Pub, Irish, Music Venues
**Average price:** Modest
**Area:** Thomas St
**Address:** 20 Bridge St Lower Dublin 8
**Phone:** 353 1 6779549

#13
**J2 Grill & Sushi**
**Cuisines:** Japanese, Sushi Bar
**Average price:** Modest
**Area:** IFSC
**Address:** Unit A, The Campshires
Dublin 1
**Phone:** 353 1 7919759

#14
**Chez Max**
**Cuisines:** French
**Average price:** Modest
**Area:** South Inner City
**Address:** 133 Lower Baggot St Dublin 2
**Phone:** 353 1 6618899

#15
### Whitefriar Grill
**Cuisines:** Irish, Breakfast & Brunch
**Average price:** Modest
**Area:** South Inner City
**Address:** 16 Aungier St Dublin 2
**Phone:** 353 1 4759003

#16
### Bison Bar & BBQ
**Cuisines:** Dive Bar, Barbeque
**Average price:** Modest
**Area:** Temple Bar
**Address:** 11 Wellington Quay Dublin 2
**Phone:** 353 86 0563144

#17
### The Porterhouse Temple Bar
**Cuisines:** Pub, Irish, Music Venues
**Average price:** Modest
**Area:** Temple Bar
**Address:** 16-18 Parliament St Dublin 2
**Phone:** 353 1 6798847

#18
### Fallon & Byrne
**Cuisines:** Wine Bar, Irish
**Average price:** Expensive
**Area:** South Inner City
**Address:** 11-17 Exchequer St Dublin 2
**Phone:** 353 1 4721010

#19
### Shanahan's On The Green
**Cuisines:** Steakhouse
**Average price:** Exclusive
**Area:** South Inner City
**Address:** 119 St. Stephens Green Dublin 2
**Phone:** 353 1 4070939

#20
### Boojum
**Cuisines:** Mexican
**Average price:** Inexpensive
**Area:** North Inner City
**Address:** Millennium Walkway Dublin 1
**Phone:** 353 1 8729499

#21
### Merchant's Arch Bar
**Cuisines:** Irish, Pub, Music Venues
**Average price:** Modest
**Area:** Temple Bar
**Address:** 48-49 Wellington Quay Dublin 2
**Phone:** 353 1 6074010

#22
### The Bakehouse
**Cuisines:** Bakery, Coffee & Tea, Breakfast & Brunch
**Average price:** Modest
**Area:** North Inner City
**Address:** 6 Bachelors Walk Dublin 1
**Phone:** 353 1 8734279

#23
### Bunsen
**Cuisines:** Burgers, Gluten-Free
**Average price:** Modest
**Area:** South Inner City
**Address:** 36 Wexford St Dublin 2
**Phone:** 353 1 5525408

#24
### Simon's Place
**Cuisines:** Coffee & Tea, Sandwiches
**Average price:** Inexpensive
**Area:** South Inner City
**Address:** 22 South Great Georges St Dublin 2
**Phone:** 353 1 6797821

#25
### Hop House - Kimchi Restaurant
**Cuisines:** Korean, Japanese
**Average price:** Modest
**Area:** Rotunda
**Address:** 160-161 Parnell St Dublin 1
**Phone:** 353 1 8728318

#26
### The Exchequer
**Cuisines:** Gastropub, Cocktail Bar
**Average price:** Modest
**Area:** South Inner City
**Address:** 3-5 Exchequer St Dublin 2
**Phone:** 353 1 6706787

#27
### Hatch and Sons
**Cuisines:** Cafe, Breakfast & Brunch
**Average price:** Modest
**Area:** South Inner City
**Address:** 15 St Stephen's Green Dublin 2
**Phone:** 353 1 6610075

#28
### The Bell & Pot
**Cuisines:** Cafe, Breakfast & Brunch
**Average price:** Modest
**Area:** South Inner City
**Address:** 3 Mercer St Dublin 2
**Phone:** 353 1 9022821

#29
**Wall & Keogh**
**Cuisines:** Tea Room, Japanese, Irish
**Average price:** Modest
**Area:** Harcourt
**Address:** 45 Richmond St S Dublin 2
**Phone:** 353 1 4759052

#30
**The Port House**
**Cuisines:** Tapas Bar
**Average price:** Modest
**Area:** South Inner City
**Address:** 64a S William St Dublin 2
**Phone:** 353 1 6770298

#31
**Red Torch Ginger**
**Cuisines:** Thai
**Average price:** Modest
**Area:** South Inner City
**Address:** 14/15 St. Andrew St Dublin 2
**Phone:** 353 1 6773363

#33
**Camden Kitchen**
**Cuisines:** European, French
**Average price:** Exclusive
**Area:** Harcourt
**Address:** 3A Camden Market Dublin 8
**Phone:** 353 1 4760125

#32
**Pearl Brasserie**
**Cuisines:** Brasserie, French
**Average price:** Exclusive
**Area:** South Inner City
**Address:** 20 Upper Merrion St Dublin 2
**Phone:** 353 1 6613572

#34
**Cafe Azteca**
**Cuisines:** Mexican
**Average price:** Modest
**Area:** South Inner City
**Address:** 19-22 Lord Edward St Dublin 2
**Phone:** 353 1 6709476

#35
**Leo Burdock**
**Cuisines:** Fast Food, Fish & Chips
**Average price:** Inexpensive
**Area:** Clanbrassil St
**Address:** 2 Werburgh St Dublin 8
**Phone:** 353 1 4540306

#36
**Elephant & Castle**
**Cuisines:** American, Breakfast & Brunch
**Average price:** Modest
**Area:** Temple Bar
**Address:** 18 Temple Bar Dublin 2
**Phone:** 353 1 6793121

#37
**Green Bench Café**
**Cuisines:** Salad, Soup, Sandwiches
**Average price:** Inexpensive
**Area:** Harcourt
**Address:** 18, Montague St Dublin 2
**Phone:** 353 1 5498229

#38
**Little Ass Burrito Bar**
**Cuisines:** Mexican
**Average price:** Inexpensive
**Area:** South Inner City
**Address:** 32a Dawson St Dublin 2
**Phone:** 353 1 7645908

#39
**The Fumbally**
**Cuisines:** Coffee & Tea
**Average price:** Modest
**Area:** Cork St
**Address:** Fumbally Court Dublin 8
**Phone:** 353 1 5298732

#40
**Darwins**
**Cuisines:** Steakhouse, Vegetarian
**Average price:** Expensive
**Area:** South Inner City
**Address:** 80 Aungier St Dublin 2
**Phone:** 353 1 4757511

#41
**The Pieman Cafe**
**Cuisines:** Cafe
**Average price:** Inexpensive
**Area:** Temple Bar
**Address:** 14a Crown Alley Dublin 2
**Phone:** 353 85 7817321

#42
**Urban Picnic**
**Cuisines:** American, Soup
**Average price:** Modest
**Area:** South Inner City
**Address:** 30 George's St Arcade
Dublin 2
**Phone:** 353 87 9775822

#43
**The Winding Stair**
**Cuisines:** Irish, European
**Average price:** Expensive
**Area:** North Inner City
**Address:** 40 Ormond Quay Dublin 1
**Phone:** 353 1 8727320

#44
**HerbSt**
**Cuisines:** Cafe
**Average price:** Modest
**Area:** Grand Canal Dock
**Address:** Hanover Quay Dublin 2
**Phone:** 353 1 6753875

#45
**Staple Foods**
**Cuisines:** Salad, Gluten-Free, Sandwiches
**Average price:** Inexpensive
**Area:** Temple Bar
**Address:** Curved St Dublin 2
**Phone:** 353 87 3902045

#46
**Musashi**
**Cuisines:** Sushi Bar, Japanese
**Average price:** Modest
**Area:** North Inner City
**Address:** 15 Capel St Dublin 1
**Phone:** 353 1 5328057

#47
**Ugly Duckling Dublin**
**Cuisines:** Coffee & Tea
**Average price:** Inexpensive
**Area:** North Inner City
**Address:** 1 Liffey Streer Lower Dublin 1
**Phone:** 353 87 3412020

#48
**Neon Asian St Food**
**Cuisines:** Thai, Asian Fusion
**Average price:** Modest
**Area:** Harcourt
**Address:** 17 Camden St Dublin 2
**Phone:** 353 1 4052222

#49
**Bibi's Cafe**
**Cuisines:** Coffee & Tea,
Breakfast & Brunch
**Average price:** Modest
**Area:** Portobello
**Address:** 14b Emorville Ave Dublin 8
**Phone:** 353 1 4547421

#50
**The Porterhouse Central**
**Cuisines:** Pub, Gastropub
**Average price:** Modest
**Area:** South Inner City
**Address:** 45-47 Nassau St Dublin 2
**Phone:** 353 1 6774180

#51
**McGrattan's In The Lane**
**Cuisines:** Pub, Irish
**Average price:** Modest
**Area:** South Inner City
**Address:** 76-77 Fitzwilliam Lane Dublin 2
**Phone:** 353 1 6618808

#52
**Listons**
**Cuisines:** Deli, Specialty Food, Salad
**Average price:** Modest
**Area:** Harcourt
**Address:** 25 Lower Camden St Dublin 2
**Phone:** 353 1 4054779

#53
**Ely Wine Bar**
**Cuisines:** Breakfast & Brunch,
Wine Bar, European
**Average price:** Modest
**Area:** South Inner City
**Address:** 22 Ely Place Dublin 2
**Phone:** 353 1 6768986

#54
**W.J. Kavanagh's**
**Cuisines:** Pub, Irish
**Average price:** Modest
**Area:** Rotunda
**Address:** 4-5 Dorset St Dublin 1
**Phone:** 353 1 8730990

#55
**Hole In The Wall**
**Cuisines:** Lounge, Gastropub
**Average price:** Modest
**Area:** Navan Rd
**Address:** Blackhorse Avenue Dublin 7
**Phone:** 353 1 8389491

#56
**Johnnie Fox's Pub**
**Cuisines:** Gastropub, Irish
**Average price:** Modest
**Area:** Glencullen
**Address:** Glencullen Dublin 18
**Phone:** 353 1 2955647

#57
**The Farm**
Cuisines: European, Irish
Average price: Modest
Area: South Inner City
Address: 3 Dawson St Dublin 2
Phone: 353 1 6718654

#58
**The Sussex**
Cuisines: Pub, Irish
Average price: Expensive
Area: Baggot St
Address: 9 Sussex Terrace Dublin 4
Phone: 353 1 6762851

#59
**Opium**
Cuisines: Vietnamese,
Cocktail Bar, Thai
Average price: Modest
Area: South Inner City
Address: 26 Wexford St Dublin 2
Phone: 353 1 5267711

#60
**The Vintage Kitchen**
Cuisines: Irish, European
Average price: Expensive
Area: South Inner City
Address: 7 Poolbeg St Dublin 2
Phone: 353 1 6798705

#61
**Cassidy's**
Cuisines: Pub, Pizza
Average price: Modest
Area: South Inner City
Address: 27 Westmoreland St Dublin 2
Phone: 353 85 8016804

#62
**The Lovely Food Company**
Cuisines: Cafe, European,
Breakfast & Brunch
Average price: Modest
Area: Terenure
Address: 14 Terenure Rd West Dublin 6
Phone: 353 1 4927717

#63
**Roly's Bistro**
Cuisines: French, European
Average price: Expensive
Area: Ballsbridge
Address: 7 Ballsbridge Terrace Dublin 4
Phone: 353 1 6682611

#64
**Aprile**
Cuisines: Burgers, Fish & Chips, Irish
Average price: Inexpensive
Area: Harcourt
Address: 46 South Richmond St Dublin 2
Phone: 353 1 4751938

#65
**The Larder**
Cuisines: European, Coffee & Tea,
Breakfast & Brunch
Average price: Modest
Area: Temple Bar
Address: 8 Parliament St Dublin 2
Phone: 353 1 6333581

#66
**Taste of Emilia**
Cuisines: Wine Bar, Deli, Italian
Average price: Modest
Area: North Inner City
Address: 1 Lower Liffey St Dublin 1
Phone: 353 1 8788188

#67
**Pitt Bros Smoked BBQ Project**
Cuisines: American, Barbeque
Average price: Modest
Area: South Inner City
Address: Wicklow House Dublin 2
Phone: 353 1 6778777

#68
**Dunne & Crescenzi**
Cuisines: Italian
Average price: Modest
Area: South Inner City
Address: 14/16 S Frederick St Dublin 2
Phone: 353 1 6773815

#69
**The Greenhouse**
Cuisines: American, Scandinavian
Average price: Exclusive
Area: South Inner City
Address: 19 Dawson St Dublin 2
Phone: 353 1 6767015

#70
**Ely Bar & Brasserie**
Cuisines: Brasserie, Wine Bar
Average price: Expensive
Area: IFSC
Address: Georges Dock, IFSC Dublin 1
Phone: 353 1 6720010

#71
## Govindas
**Cuisines:** Vegetarian
**Average price:** Inexpensive
**Area:** North Inner City
**Address:** 83 Middle Abbey St Dublin 1
**Phone:** 353 1 8728961

#72
## Junos Cafe
**Cuisines:** Sandwiches, Irish, Cafe
**Average price:** Modest
**Area:** Phoneix Park
**Address:** 26 Parkgate St Dublin 8
**Phone:** 353 1 6709820

#73
## Odessa
**Cuisines:** Breakfast & Brunch,
Brasserie, Wine Bar
**Average price:** Modest
**Area:** South Inner City
**Address:** 13/14 Dame Court Dublin 2
**Phone:** 353 1 6703080

#74
## Il Valentino
**Cuisines:** Bakery, Cafe
**Average price:** Inexpensive
**Area:** Grand Canal Dock
**Address:** 5 Gallery Quay Dublin 2
**Phone:** 353 1 6331100

#75
## Thai Spice
**Cuisines:** Thai
**Average price:** Modest
**Area:** Gardiner St
**Address:** 3a Talbot Place Dublin 1
**Phone:** 353 1 8550226

#76
## Jo 'Burger
**Cuisines:** Burgers
**Average price:** Modest
**Area:** Rathmines
**Address:** 137 Rathmines Rd Dublin 6
**Phone:** 353 1 4913731

#77
## Mayfield Deli & Eatery
**Cuisines:** Deli
**Average price:** Modest
**Area:** Terenure
**Address:** Terenure Rd N Dublin 6w
**Phone:** 353 1 4926830

#78
## Avoca
**Cuisines:** Irish, Home Decor,
Department Store
**Average price:** Modest
**Area:** Rathcoole
**Address:** N7 Naas Rd Dublin
**Phone:** 353 1 2571810

#79
## Café Topolis
**Cuisines:** Italian
**Average price:** Modest
**Area:** South Inner City
**Address:** 37 Parliament St Dublin 2
**Phone:** 353 1 6704961

#80
## Baan Thai
**Cuisines:** Thai
**Average price:** Expensive
**Area:** Ballsbridge
**Address:** 16 Merrion Rd Dublin 4
**Phone:** 353 1 6608833

#81
## Antoinette's Bakery
**Cuisines:** Bakery, Coffee & Tea,
Gluten-Free
**Average price:** Modest
**Area:** South Inner City
**Address:** 6 Kevin St Lower Dublin 8
**Phone:** 353 1 4759008

#82
## Zaytoon
**Cuisines:** Persian/Iranian,
Fast Food, Kebab
**Average price:** Modest
**Area:** Harcourt
**Address:** 44-45 Lower Camden St Dublin 2
**Phone:** 353 1 4005006

#83
## Patrick Guilbaud Restaurant
**Cuisines:** European
**Average price:** Exclusive
**Area:** South Inner City
**Address:** 21 Upper Merrion St Dublin 2
**Phone:** 353 1 6764192

#84
## Peploes
**Cuisines:** Brasserie, French
**Average price:** Expensive
**Area:** South Inner City
**Address:** 16 St Stephens Green Dublin 2
**Phone:** 353 1 6763144

#85
**Probus Wines & Spirits Dublin**
Cuisines: Beer, Wine, Spirits, Cafe
Average price: Modest
Area: South Inner City
Address: 26 Fenian St Dublin 2
Phone: 353 1 6629649

#86
**Ciao Bella Roma**
Cuisines: Italian, Pizza
Average price: Modest
Area: Temple Bar
Address: 25 Parliament St Dublin 2
Phone: 353 1 6770004

#87
**The Green Hen**
Cuisines: Brasserie, French
Average price: Expensive
Area: South Inner City
Address: 33 Exchequer St Dublin 2
Phone: 353 1 6707238

#88
**The Chop House**
Cuisines: Gastropub
Average price: Expensive
Area: Beggars Bush
Address: 2 Shelbourne Rd Dublin 4
Phone: 353 1 6602390

#89
**Kennedy's Food Store**
Cuisines: Irish, Coffee & Tea, Deli
Average price: Modest
Area: Marino
Address: 5 Fairview Strand Dublin 3
Phone: 353 1 8331400

#90
**Ryans Of Parkgate St**
Cuisines: Steakhouse
Average price: Modest
Area: Phoneix Park
Address: 28 Parkgate St Dublin 8
Phone: 353 1 6776097

#91
**Burritos & Blues**
Cuisines: Mexican
Average price: Inexpensive
Area: South Inner City
Address: 2 Wexford St Dublin 2
Phone: 353 86 3000500

#92
**Pablo Picanté**
Cuisines: Mexican
Average price: Inexpensive
Area: South Inner City
Address: 131 Baggot St Dublin 2
Phone: 353 1 6629773

#93
**101 Talbot Restaurant**
Cuisines: European
Average price: Modest
Area: North Inner City
Address: 101-102 Talbot St Dublin 1
Phone: 353 1 8745011

#94
**Pichet**
Cuisines: Brasserie, Coffee & Tea
Average price: Expensive
Area: South Inner City
Address: 14-15 Trinity St Dublin 2
Phone: 353 1 6771060

#95
**Le Bon Crubeen**
Cuisines: French, Jazz & Blues
Average price: Expensive
Area: North Inner City
Address: 81-82 Talbot St Dublin 1
Phone: 353 1 7040126

#96
**The Mongolian Barbeque**
Cuisines: Mongolian, Buffets
Average price: Inexpensive
Area: Temple Bar
Address: 7 Anglesea St Dublin 2
Phone: 353 1 6704154

#97
**Chez Max**
Cuisines: French
Average price: Expensive
Area: South Inner City
Address: 1 Palace St Dublin 2
Phone: 353 1 6337215

#98
**Little Jerusalem**
Cuisines: Middle Eastern
Average price: Modest
Area: Rathmines
Address: 3 Wynnefield Rd Dublin 6
Phone: 353 1 4126912

#99
**Soulful Bistro**
**Cuisines:** Irish, Soul Food,
Breakfast & Brunch
**Average price:** Modest
**Area:** Stoneybatter
**Address:** 46 Manor St Dublin 7
**Phone:** 353 1 8688400

#100
**Millstone Restaurant**
**Cuisines:** European
**Average price:** Modest
**Area:** South Inner City
**Address:** 39 Dame St Dublin 2
**Phone:** 353 1 6799931

#101
**ZAKURA**
**Cuisines:** Sushi Bar, Japanese
**Average price:** Modest
**Area:** South Inner City
**Address:** 13 Wexford St Dublin 2
**Phone:** 353 1 5558000

#102
**The Counter**
**Cuisines:** Burgers, American
**Average price:** Modest
**Area:** South Inner City
**Address:** 20 Suffolk St Dublin 2
**Phone:** 353 1 6111689

#103
**Travel Cafe & Restaurant**
**Cuisines:** French, Steakhouse, Pizza
**Average price:** Modest
**Area:** Dún Laoghaire
**Address:** Unit 2, Harbour Square Dublin
**Phone:** 353 1 5512656

#104
**O'Neills Bar & Restaurant**
**Cuisines:** Irish, Pub
**Average price:** Modest
**Area:** South Inner City
**Address:** 2 Suffolk St Dublin 2
**Phone:** 353 1 6793656

#105
**The Boar's Head**
**Cuisines:** Irish, Pub
**Average price:** Modest
**Area:** North Inner City
**Address:** 149 Capel St Dublin 1
**Phone:** 353 1 8723107

#106
**Matt The Thresher**
**Cuisines:** Seafood
**Average price:** Expensive
**Area:** South Inner City
**Address:** 31 -32 Lower Pembroke St
Dublin 2
**Phone:** 353 1 6762980

#107
**Pablo Picanté**
**Cuisines:** Mexican
**Average price:** Inexpensive
**Area:** Temple Bar
**Address:** 22 Temple Bar Dublin 2
**Phone:** 353 1 6791000

#108
**Bang Restaurant**
**Cuisines:** Irish, European, Wine Bar
**Average price:** Expensive
**Area:** South Inner City
**Address:** 11 Merrion Row Dublin 2
**Phone:** 353 1 4004229

#109
**Sabor Brazil**
**Cuisines:** Brazilian
**Average price:** Exclusive
**Area:** Harcourt
**Address:** 50 Pleasants St Dublin 8
**Phone:** 353 1 4750304

#110
**Las Tapas de Lola**
**Cuisines:** Tapas Bar, Spanish
**Average price:** Modest
**Area:** South Inner City
**Address:** Wexford St Dublin 2
**Phone:** 353 1 4244100

#111
**Kinara Restaurant**
**Cuisines:** Pakistani
**Average price:** Expensive
**Area:** Clontarf
**Address:** 318 Clontarf Rd Dublin 3
**Phone:** 353 1 8336759

#112
**K Chido Mexico**
**Cuisines:** Mexican, Food Stand,
StreetVendor
**Average price:** Inexpensive
**Area:** Four Courts
**Address:** Chancery St Dublin 7
**Phone:** 353 86 3534369

#113
**Enoteca Delle Langhe**
**Cuisines:** Italian, Wine Bar
**Average price:** Modest
**Area:** North Inner City
**Address:** Blooms Lane Dublin 1
**Phone:** 353 1 8880834

#114
**Urbun**
**Cuisines:** Cafe
**Average price:** Modest
**Area:** Cabinteely
**Address:** Old Bray Rd Dublin 18
**Phone:** 353 1 2848872

#115
**The Cedar Tree**
**Cuisines:** Middle Eastern, Mediterranean
**Average price:** Modest
**Area:** South Inner City
**Address:** 11 St. Andrews St Dublin 2
**Phone:** 353 1 6772121

#116
**China Sichuan Restaurant**
**Cuisines:** Chinese, Bistro, Brasserie
**Average price:** Expensive
**Area:** Sandyford
**Address:** The Forum Ballymoss Rd
Dublin 18
**Phone:** 353 1 2935100

#117
**Arisu Korean Restaurant**
**Cuisines:** Korean, Sushi Bar, Barbeque
**Average price:** Modest
**Area:** North Inner City
**Address:** 119 Capel St Dublin 1
**Phone:** 353 1 5158022

#118
**Rustic Stone**
**Cuisines:** American, Irish
**Average price:** Expensive
**Area:** South Inner City
**Address:** 17 S Great Georges St
Dublin 2
**Phone:** 353 1 7079596

#119
**Caffe Cagliostro**
**Cuisines:** Italian, Coffee & Tea
**Average price:** Inexpensive
**Area:** North Inner City
**Address:** 24 Ormond Quay Lower
Dublin 1
**Phone:** 353 1 8880860

#120
**The Pig and Heifer**
**Cuisines:** Deli, Sandwiches,
Coffee & Tea
**Average price:** Inexpensive
**Area:** South Inner City
**Address:** 21-23 City Quay Dublin 2
**Phone:** 353 1 6336972

#121
**Diwali Indian Restaurant**
**Cuisines:** Indian, Himalayan/Nepalese
**Average price:** Modest
**Area:** South Inner City
**Address:** South Great Georges St Dublin 2
**Phone:** 353 1 4750091

#122
**Pablo Picante**
**Cuisines:** Mexican
**Average price:** Inexpensive
**Area:** South Inner City
**Address:** Clarendon Market Dublin 2
**Phone:** 353 1 6334245

#123
**Bóbós Burgers Restaurant**
**Cuisines:** Burgers
**Average price:** Modest
**Area:** South Inner City
**Address:** 50-51 Dame St Dublin 2
**Phone:** 353 1 6722025

#124
**DiFontaine's Pizzeria**
**Cuisines:** Pizza, Fast Food
**Average price:** Inexpensive
**Area:** Temple Bar
**Address:** 22 Parliament St Dublin 2
**Phone:** 353 1 6745485

#125
**The Auld Dubliner**
**Cuisines:** Pub, Irish
**Average price:** Modest
**Area:** Temple Bar
**Address:** 24-25 Temple Bar Dublin 2
**Phone:** 353 1 6770527

#126
**Seagrass Restaurant**
**Cuisines:** European, Irish,
Breakfast & Brunch
**Average price:** Modest
**Area:** Harcourt
**Address:** 30 S Richmond St Dublin 2
**Phone:** 353 1 4789595

#127
**Rotana Café**
**Cuisines:** Middle Eastern
**Average price:** Modest
**Area:** Harcourt
**Address:** 31 South Richmond St Dublin 2
**Phone:** 353 1 4759969

#128
**The Exchange Restaurant
& Cocktail Bar**
**Cuisines:** American, Bar, Irish
**Average price:** Expensive
**Area:** South Inner City
**Address:** At College Green
Westmoreland St Dublin 2
**Phone:** 353 1 6451318

#129
**Il Caffè di Napoli**
**Cuisines:** Coffee & Tea, Italian, Sandwiches
**Average price:** Expensive
**Area:** South Inner City
**Address:** 41 Westland Row Dublin 2
**Phone:** 353 1 6114831

#130
**La Maison**
**Cuisines:** French, Seafood
**Average price:** Expensive
**Area:** South Inner City
**Address:** 15 Castle Market Dublin 2
**Phone:** 353 1 6727258

#131
**Seasons Restaurant**
**Cuisines:** American, Sushi Bar
**Average price:** Modest
**Area:** Ballsbridge
**Address:** Simmonscourt Rd Dublin 4
**Phone:** 353 35 36654000

#132
**Cafe En Seine**
**Cuisines:** Pub, Gastropub
**Average price:** Modest
**Area:** South Inner City
**Address:** 40 Dawson St Dublin 2
**Phone:** 353 1 6774567

#133
**The Birdcage Bakery**
**Cuisines:** Cafe, Bakery
**Average price:** Inexpensive
**Area:** Harcourt
**Address:** 21 Harcourt Rd Dublin 2
**Phone:** 353 1 4783820

#134
**Keshk Cafe & Restaurant**
**Cuisines:** Mediterranean,
Middle Eastern
**Average price:** Modest
**Area:** Baggot St
**Address:** 71 Mespil Rd Dublin 4
**Phone:** 353 1 6673002

#135
**The Grand Social**
**Cuisines:** Irish, Music Venues, Pub
**Average price:** Modest
**Area:** North Inner City
**Address:** 35 Lower Liffey St Dublin 1
**Phone:** 353 1 8740076

#136
**Lord Edward Seafood Restaurant**
**Cuisines:** Pub, Seafood
**Average price:** Modest
**Area:** Clanbrassil St
**Address:** 23 Christchurch Pl Dublin 8
**Phone:** 353 1 4542420

#137
**FX Buckley**
**Cuisines:** Steakhouse
**Average price:** Expensive
**Area:** South Inner City
**Address:** 1A Lower Pembroke St Dublin 2
**Phone:** 353 1 6764606

#138
**Kafka**
**Cuisines:** European
**Average price:** Modest
**Area:** Rathmines
**Address:** 236 Lower Rathmines Rd Dublin 6
**Phone:** 353 1 4977057

#139
**Michie Sushi**
**Cuisines:** Sushi Bar, Japanese
**Average price:** Modest
**Area:** Rathgar
**Address:** 11 Chelmsford Lane Dublin 6
**Phone:** 353 1 4976438

#140
**Farmer Browns**
**Cuisines:** Irish, Burgers,
Breakfast & Brunch
**Average price:** Modest
**Area:** Beggars Bush
**Address:** 25A Bath Avenue Dublin 4
**Phone:** 353 1 6602326

#141
**147 Deli**
**Cuisines:** Delicatessen, Cafe
**Average price:** Inexpensive
**Area:** Rotunda
**Address:** 147 Parnell St Dublin 1
**Phone:** 353 87 9166116

#142
**L'Gueuleton**
**Cuisines:** French
**Average price:** Expensive
**Area:** South Inner City
**Address:** 1 Fade St Dublin 2
**Phone:** 353 1 6753708

#143
**Locks Brasserie**
**Cuisines:** French, Irish, Brasserie
**Average price:** Expensive
**Area:** Portobello
**Address:** 1 Windsor Terrace Dublin 8
**Phone:** 353 1 4200555

#144
**Honest to Goodness**
**Cuisines:** Coffee & Tea, Sandwiches
**Average price:** Modest
**Area:** South Inner City
**Address:** 12 Dame Court Dublin 2
**Phone:** 353 1 6337727

#145
**Yamamori Izakaya**
**Cuisines:** Japanese, Bar
**Average price:** Modest
**Area:** South Inner City
**Address:** 12-13 S Great George's St
Dublin 2
**Phone:** 353 1 6458001

#146
**The House**
**Cuisines:** Irish, Seafood,
Breakfast & Brunch
**Average price:** Expensive
**Area:** Howth
**Address:** 4 Main St Dublin 11
**Phone:** 353 1 8396388

#147
**Steps Of Rome**
**Cuisines:** Italian, Pizza
**Average price:** Modest
**Area:** South Inner City
**Address:** 1 Chatham Court Dublin 2
**Phone:** 353 1 6705630

#148
**Dux & Co.**
**Cuisines:** Irish, Caterers, European
**Average price:** Modest
**Area:** Temple Bar
**Address:** 51 Wellington Quay Dublin 2
**Phone:** 353 1 6139864

#149
**Bear**
**Cuisines:** Steakhouse
**Average price:** Expensive
**Area:** South Inner City
**Address:** 34-35 South William St Dublin 2
**Phone:** 353 1 4744888

#150
**Bagots Hutton Wine Emporium**
**Cuisines:** Mediterranean, Wine Bar
**Average price:** Modest
**Area:** South Inner City
**Address:** 28 S William St Dublin 2
**Phone:** 353 1 5343956

#151
**The Canal Bank Cafe**
**Cuisines:** Burgers, Sandwiches
**Average price:** Modest
**Area:** Baggot St
**Address:** 146 Upper Leeson St Dublin 4
**Phone:** 353 1 6642135

#152
**Sinnotts**
**Cuisines:** Pub, Sports Bar, Gastropub
**Average price:** Modest
**Area:** South Inner City
**Address:** South King St Dublin 2
**Phone:** 353 1 4784698

#153
**Musashi IFSC**
**Cuisines:** Sushi Bar
**Average price:** Modest
**Area:** IFSC
**Address:** Unit 2 Custom House
Square Dublin 1
**Phone:** 353 1 5557373

#154
**KonKan**
**Cuisines:** Indian
**Average price:** Modest
**Area:** Portobello
**Address:** 46 Upper Clanbrassil St Dublin 8
**Phone:** 353 1 4738252

#155
**The Runner Bean**
**Cuisines:** Salad, Vegetarian
**Average price:** Inexpensive
**Area:** South Inner City
**Address:** 4 Nassau St Dublin 2
**Phone:** 353 1 6794833

#156
**Pygmalion Café**
**Cuisines:** Irish, Cafe
**Average price:** Expensive
**Area:** South Inner City
**Address:** 59 South William St Dublin 2
**Phone:** 353 1 6779490

#157
**The French Paradox**
**Cuisines:** French, Wine Bar,
Breakfast & Brunch
**Average price:** Expensive
**Area:** Ballsbridge
**Address:** 53 Shelbourne Rd Dublin 4
**Phone:** 353 1 6604068

#158
**Pizzicato**
**Cuisines:** Pizza, Italian
**Average price:** Modest
**Area:** Sandyford
**Address:** 21 Corrig Rd Dublin 18
**Phone:** 353 1 2973461

#159
**Etto**
**Cuisines:** Irish
**Average price:** Expensive
**Area:** South Inner City
**Address:** 18 Merrion Row Dublin 2
**Phone:** 353 1 6788872

#160
**Marco Pierre White**
**Cuisines:** Steakhouse
**Average price:** Expensive
**Area:** South Inner City
**Address:** 51 Dawson St Dublin 2
**Phone:** 353 1 6771155

#161
**Soup Dragon**
**Cuisines:** Soup, Coffee & Tea,
Breakfast & Brunch
**Average price:** Inexpensive
**Area:** North Inner City
**Address:** 168 Capel St Dublin 1
**Phone:** 353 1 8723277

#162
**The Pig & Heifer**
**Cuisines:** Deli, Coffee & Tea
**Average price:** Inexpensive
**Area:** South Inner City
**Address:** 151 Pearse St Dublin 2
**Phone:** 353 1 6753714

#163
**The Temple Bar**
**Cuisines:** Pub, Gastropub
**Average price:** Modest
**Area:** Temple Bar
**Address:** 47/48 Temple Bar Dublin 2
**Phone:** 353 1 6725286

#164
**Mulberry Garden**
**Cuisines:** Irish
**Average price:** Expensive
**Area:** Ballsbridge
**Address:** Mulberry Lane Dublin 4
**Phone:** 353 1 2693300

#165
**Aqua**
**Cuisines:** Seafood
**Average price:** Expensive
**Area:** Howth
**Address:** 1 West Pier Dublin 13
**Phone:** 353 1 8320690

#166
**The Market Bar**
**Cuisines:** Bar, Tapas Bar, European
**Average price:** Modest
**Area:** South Inner City
**Address:** 14 Fade St Dublin 2
**Phone:** 353 1 6139094

#167
**Downstairs**
**Cuisines:** Irish, Brasserie
**Average price:** Expensive
**Area:** Clontarf
**Address:** Hollybrook Park Dublin 3
**Phone:** 353 1 8338883

#168
**The Hairy Lemon**
**Cuisines:** Pub, Gastropub
**Average price:** Modest
**Area:** South Inner City
**Address:** Stephen St Dublin 2
**Phone:** 353 1 6718949

#169
**The Pyg Restaurant**
**Cuisines:** European, Tapas
**Average price:** Modest
**Area:** South Inner City
**Address:** South William St Dublin 2
**Phone:** 353 1 6779490

#170
**Umi Falafel**
**Cuisines:** Vegetarian, Falafel,
Middle Eastern
**Average price:** Inexpensive
**Area:** South Inner City
**Address:** 13 Dame St Dublin 2
**Phone:** 353 1 6706866

#171
**Gammells**
**Cuisines:** Deli, Bakery, Coffee & Tea
**Average price:** Inexpensive
**Area:** Rathgar
**Address:** 33 Ranelagh Rd Dublin 6
**Phone:** 353 1 4962311

#172
**Enoteca D'Asti**
**Cuisines:** Italian
**Average price:** Expensive
**Area:** Ballybough
**Address:** 15 Russell St Dublin 3
**Phone:** 353 1 8847500

#173
**The Waterloo Bar & Grill**
**Cuisines:** Pub, Gastropub, Cocktail Bar
**Average price:** Modest
**Area:** Baggot St
**Address:** 36 Upper Baggot St Dublin 4
**Phone:** 353 1 6600650

#174
**Mother Reilly's**
**Cuisines:** Pub, European, Irish
**Average price:** Modest
**Area:** Rathgar
**Address:** 30-32 Upper Rathmines Rd
Dublin 6
**Phone:** 353 1 4975486

#175
**Cafe Bliss**
**Cuisines:** Coffee & Tea, European
**Average price:** Inexpensive
**Area:** South Inner City
**Address:** 4B Montague St Dublin 2
**Phone:** 353 1 4781600

#176
**Bleecker St. Cafe Bar**
**Cuisines:** American, Cafe, Cocktail Bar
**Average price:** Modest
**Area:** Rotunda
**Address:** 68 Dorset St Dublin 1
**Phone:** 353 1 8044459

#177
**Lemon Jelly Cafe**
**Cuisines:** Creperies, Juice Bar, Cafe
**Average price:** Modest
**Area:** North Inner City
**Address:** Jervis St Dublin 1
**Phone:** 353 1 8735161

#178
**The Parnell Heritage Pub & Grill**
**Cuisines:** Sports Bar, Gastropub
**Average price:** Modest
**Area:** North Inner City
**Address:** 72-74 Parnell St Dublin 1
**Phone:** 353 1 8783380

#179
**Caffe' Italiano**
**Cuisines:** Italian
**Average price:** Modest
**Area:** Temple Bar
**Address:** 7 Crow St Dublin 2
**Phone:** 353 1 5511206

#180
**HX46**
**Cuisines:** Coffee & Tea, Asian Fusion
**Average price:** Modest
**Area:** Harold's Cross
**Address:** 46 Harold's Cross Rd
Dublin 6w
**Phone:** 353 1 5385000

#181
**Han Sung**
**Cuisines:** Korean, Grocery
**Average price:** Inexpensive
**Area:** North Inner City
**Address:** 22 Great Strand St Dublin 1
**Phone:** 353 1 8874405

#182
**The Saddle Room Restaurant**
**Cuisines:** Diner
**Average price:** Expensive
**Area:** South Inner City
**Address:** 27 St Stephen's Green
Dublin 2
**Phone:** 353 1 6634500

#183
**Independent Pizza Company**
**Cuisines:** Pizza
**Average price:** Modest
**Area:** Drumcondra
**Address:** 28 Drumcondra Rd Lower Dublin 9
**Phone:** 353 1 8302044

#184
**Salamanca**
**Cuisines:** Spanish, Tapas
**Average price:** Expensive
**Area:** South Inner City
**Address:** 1 St Andrew St Dublin 2
**Phone:** 353 1 6774799

#185
**Bombay Pantry Ashtown**
**Cuisines:** Indian
**Average price:** Modest
**Area:** Navan Rd
**Address:** Rathbourne Village Dublin 15
**Phone:** 353 1 8996688

#186
**Bistro One**
**Cuisines:** Italian
**Average price:** Expensive
**Area:** Cabinteely
**Address:** 3 Brighton Rd Dublin 18
**Phone:** 353 1 2897711

#187
**Blackboard Bistro**
**Cuisines:** French
**Average price:** Expensive
**Area:** South Inner City
**Address:** 4 Clare St Dublin 2
**Phone:** 353 1 6766839

#188
**Zaytoon**
**Cuisines:** Persian/Iranian,
Fast Food, Kebab
**Average price:** Inexpensive
**Area:** Temple Bar
**Address:** 14-15 Parliament St Dublin 2
**Phone:** 353 1 6773595

#189
**The Church**
**Cuisines:** Bar, Irish, Cafe
**Average price:** Modest
**Area:** North Inner City
**Address:** Mary St Dublin 1
**Phone:** 353 1 8280102

#190
**Manifesto**
**Cuisines:** Italian, Gluten-Free
**Average price:** Modest
**Area:** Rathmines
**Address:** 208 Lower Rathmines Rd Dublin 6
**Phone:** 353 1 4968096

#191
**Govinda's**
**Cuisines:** Vegetarian, Caterers
**Average price:** Inexpensive
**Area:** South Inner City
**Address:** 4 Aungier St Dublin 2
**Phone:** 353 1 4750309

#192
**LIBERTÉ**
**Cuisines:** French
**Average price:** Modest
**Area:** Harcourt
**Address:** Vault 4 Dublin 2
**Phone:** 353 1 4110097

#193
**San Lorenzo's**
**Cuisines:** Italian, Breakfast & Brunch
**Average price:** Modest
**Area:** South Inner City
**Address:** S Great Georges St Dublin 2
**Phone:** 353 1 4789383

#194
**Credo Pizza**
**Cuisines:** Pizza, Italian,
Food Delivery Services
**Average price:** Modest
**Area:** Harcourt
**Address:** 19 Montague St Dublin 2
**Phone:** 353 1 4780500

#195
**Ray's Pizza**
**Cuisines:** Pizza
**Average price:** Inexpensive
**Area:** Harcourt
**Address:** 17 Harcourt Rd Dublin 2
**Phone:** 353 1 4752190

#196
**Vermilion**
**Cuisines:** Indian
**Average price:** Modest
**Area:** Terenure
**Address:** 94/96 Terenure Rd
N Dublin 6w
**Phone:** 353 1 4991400

#197
**Cleaver East**
**Cuisines:** Seafood, Steakhouse
**Average price:** Modest
**Area:** Temple Bar
**Address:** East Essex St Dublin 2
**Phone:** 353 1 5313500

#198
**Rigbys Deli & Dining Room**
**Cuisines:** Deli
**Average price:** Modest
**Area:** Baggot St
**Address:** 126 Upper Leeson St Dublin 4
**Phone:** 353 87 7939195

#199
**La Dolce Vita Sandyford**
**Cuisines:** Italian
**Average price:** Modest
**Area:** Sandyford
**Address:** Carmanhall Rd Dublin
**Phone:** 353 1 2946903

#200
**The Pig & Heifer**
**Cuisines:** Coffee & Tea, Deli
**Average price:** Inexpensive
**Area:** Harcourt
**Address:** 2 Charlotte Way Dublin 2
**Phone:** 353 1 4783182

#201
**Pho Viet**
**Cuisines:** Vietnamese
**Average price:** Modest
**Area:** Rotunda
**Address:** 162 Parnell St Dublin 1
**Phone:** 353 1 8783165

#202
**Bite of Life Food Co.**
**Cuisines:** Coffee & Tea,
Breakfast & Brunch, Sandwiches
**Average price:** Inexpensive
**Area:** Clanbrassil St
**Address:** 55 Patrick St Dublin 8
**Phone:** 353 1 4542949

#203
**Blazing Salads**
**Cuisines:** Vegetarian, Salad, Vegan
**Average price:** Inexpensive
**Area:** South Inner City
**Address:** 42 Drury St Dublin 2
**Phone:** 353 1 6719552

#204
**Terra Madre**
**Cuisines:** Italian
**Average price:** Modest
**Area:** North Inner City
**Address:** 13a Bachelors Walk Dublin 1
**Phone:** 353 1 8735300

#205
**Mama's Revenge**
**Cuisines:** Mexican
**Average price:** Inexpensive
**Area:** South Inner City
**Address:** 12 Leinster St S Dublin 2
**Phone:** 353 86 3702654

#206
**Montys of Kathmandu**
**Cuisines:** Himalayan/Nepalese, Indian
**Average price:** Expensive
**Area:** South Inner City
**Address:** 28 Eustace St Dublin 2
**Phone:** 353 1 6704911

#207
**Donnybrook Fair**
**Cuisines:** Deli, Grocery
**Average price:** Expensive
**Area:** Milltown, Ballsbridge
**Address:** 89 Morehampton Rd Dublin 4
**Phone:** 353 1 6683556

#208
**Phx Bistro**
**Cuisines:** Irish
**Average price:** Modest
**Area:** Collins Barracks
**Address:** 12 Ellis Quay Dublin 7
**Phone:** 353 1 6111161

#209
**Joels**
**Cuisines:** Steakhouse, Chicken Wings
**Average price:** Modest
**Area:** Clondalkin
**Address:** N7 Naas Rd Dublin 22
**Phone:** 353 1 4592968

#210
**BirchHall**
**Cuisines:** Pub, Gastropub
**Average price:** Modest
**Area:** Rathgar
**Address:** 120 Ranelagh Dublin 6
**Phone:** 353 1 4973985

#211
**Lolly and Cooks**
**Cuisines:** Cafe, Bakery
**Average price:** Modest
**Area:** South Inner City
**Address:** 18 Upper Merrion St Dublin 2
**Phone:** 353 1 6624313

#212
**Dublin Wine Room**
**Cuisines:** Irish, Seafood, Wine Bar
**Average price:** Modest
**Area:** IFSC
**Address:** Custom House Square Dublin 1
**Phone:** 353 1 6360616

#213
**The Schoolhouse Bar**
**& Restaurant**
**Cuisines:** Gastropub, Pub, French,
European
**Average price:** Modest
**Area:** Beggars Bush
**Address:** 2-8 Northumberland Rd Dublin 4
**Phone:** 353 1 6675014

#214
**Bottega Toffoli**
**Cuisines:** Italian
**Average price:** Modest
**Area:** South Inner City
**Address:** 34 Castle St Dublin 2
**Phone:** 353 1 6334022

#215
**La Corte**
**Cuisines:** Italian
**Average price:** Inexpensive
**Area:** North Inner City
**Address:** Epicurean Food Hall
Liffey St Dublin 1
**Phone:** 353 1 8734200

#216
**Toscana Restaurant City Centre**
**Cuisines:** Italian, Pizza
**Average price:** Modest
**Area:** South Inner City
**Address:** 3 Cork Hill Dublin 2
**Phone:** 353 1 6709785

#217
**Food Game**
**Cuisines:** Breakfast & Brunch
**Average price:** Expensive
**Area:** Beggars Bush
**Address:** 10 S Lotts Rd Dublin 4
**Phone:** 353 1 2815002

#218
**Clarke's Home Bakery**
**Cuisines:** Bakery, Breakfast & Brunch
**Average price:** Expensive
**Area:** Cabra
**Address:** 54 New Cabra Rd Dublin 7
**Phone:** 353 1 8389724

#219
**777**
**Cuisines:** Mexican
**Average price:** Exclusive
**Area:** South Inner City
**Address:** 7 South Great George's St
Dublin 2
**Phone:** 353 1 4254052

#220
**Residence**
**Cuisines:** European, Wine Bar
**Average price:** Exclusive
**Area:** South Inner City
**Address:** 41 St. Stephen's Green Dublin 2
**Phone:** 353 1 6620000

#221
**Skinflint**
**Cuisines:** Pizza, Italian
**Average price:** Modest
**Area:** South Inner City
**Address:** 19 Crane Lane Dublin 2
**Phone:** 353 1 6709719

#222
**The Gallery Cafe & Restauraunt**
**Cuisines:** Coffee & Tea, Irish
**Average price:** Modest
**Area:** Whitehall
**Address:** Swords Rd Dublin 9
**Phone:** 353 1 7044005

#223
**Bay**
**Cuisines:** Irish
**Average price:** Expensive
**Area:** Clontarf
**Address:** 367 Clontarf Rd Dublin 3
**Phone:** 353 1 8532406

#224
**Nelly's**
**Cuisines:** Sandwiches, Cafe
**Average price:** Inexpensive
**Area:** Portobello
**Address:** 12 S Circular Rd Dublin 8
**Phone:** 353 1 4734775

#225
**Brownes**
**Cuisines:** Deli, Breakfast & Brunch,
Coffee & Tea
**Average price:** Modest
**Area:** Irishtown
**Address:** 18 Sandymount Green Dublin 4
**Phone:** 353 1 2697316

#226
**Walters Café Bar & Restaurant**
**Cuisines:** Gastropub, Pub, Cafe
**Average price:** Modest
**Area:** Dún Laoghaire
**Address:** 68 Upper Georges St Dublin
**Phone:** 353 1 2807442

#227
**Burritos & Blues**
**Cuisines:** Mexican
**Average price:** Inexpensive
**Area:** East Wall
**Address:** 4 Mayor St Dublin 1
**Phone:** 353 1 6116940

#228
**Chopped**
**Cuisines:** Salad, Vegetarian, Juice Bar
**Average price:** Inexpensive
**Area:** South Inner City
**Address:** Baggot St Lower Dublin 2
**Phone:** 353 1 6766838

#229
**House**
**Cuisines:** Bar, Mediterranean
**Average price:** Expensive
**Area:** Harcourt
**Address:** 27 Lower Leeson St Dublin 2
**Phone:** 353 1 9059090

#230
**Davy Byrnes**
**Cuisines:** Gastropub
**Average price:** Modest
**Area:** South Inner City
**Address:** 21 Duke St Dublin 2
**Phone:** 353 1 6775217

#231
**TriBeCa Restaurant**
**Cuisines:** American, Burgers, Sandwiches
**Average price:** Modest
**Area:** Rathgar
**Address:** 65 Ranelagh Dublin 6
**Phone:** 353 1 4974174

#232
**Bóbós**
**Cuisines:** Burgers
**Average price:** Modest
**Area:** South Inner City
**Address:** 22 Wexford St Dublin 2
**Phone:** 353 1 4005750

#233
**Fire**
**Cuisines:** Brasserie, European, Irish
**Average price:** Expensive
**Area:** South Inner City
**Address:** Dawson St Dublin 2
**Phone:** 353 1 6767200

#234
**Super Miss Sue**
**Cuisines:** Fish & Chips, Seafood
**Average price:** Expensive
**Area:** South Inner City
**Address:** Stephen St Lower Dublin 2
**Phone:** 353 1 6799009

#235
**Farm Restaurant**
**Cuisines:** Irish, European
**Average price:** Expensive
**Area:** Baggot St
**Address:** 133 Upper Leeson St Dublin 2
**Phone:** 353 1 2120743

#236
**Andersons Creperie**
**Cuisines:** Creperies
**Average price:** Modest
**Area:** Drumcondra
**Address:** 1A Carlingord Rd Dublin 9
**Phone:** 353 1 8305171

#237
**The Greenery Restaurant
Donnybrook**
**Cuisines:** Tea Room, Cafe
**Average price:** Modest
**Area:** Donnybrook
**Address:** Eirpage House Dublin 4
**Phone:** 353 1 2195966

#238
**Pablo's Tortas**
**Cuisines:** Mexican
**Average price:** Inexpensive
**Area:** South Inner City
**Address:** 5 Clarendon Market Dublin 2
**Phone:** 353 1 6334245

#239
**Lemon**
**Cuisines:** Creperies, Coffee & Tea
**Average price:** Inexpensive
**Area:** South Inner City
**Address:** 60 Dawson St Dublin 2
**Phone:** 353 1 6728898

#240
**Nancy Hands Bar & Restaurant**
**Cuisines:** American
**Average price:** Modest
**Area:** Phoneix Park
**Address:** 30-32 Parkgate St Dublin 8
**Phone:** 353 1 6770149

#241
**The Hot Stove Restaurant**
**Cuisines:** Irish
**Average price:** Exclusive
**Area:** Parnell Square
**Address:** 38 Parnell Square W Dublin 1
**Phone:** 353 1 8747778

#242
**Seapoint Fish & Grill**
**Cuisines:** Seafood
**Average price:** Expensive
**Area:** Dún Laoghaire
**Address:** 4 Monkstown Crescent Dublin
**Phone:** 353 1 6638480

#243
**The Cellar Restaurant**
**Cuisines:** Cafe
**Average price:** Exclusive
**Area:** South Inner City
**Address:** Upper Merrion St Dublin 2
**Phone:** 353 1 6030600

#244
**FXB**
**Cuisines:** Steakhouse, Irish
**Average price:** Expensive
**Area:** Temple Bar
**Address:** 2 Crow St Dublin 2
**Phone:** 353 1 6711248

#245
**La Bodega**
**Cuisines:** Tapas Bar, Spanish
**Average price:** Expensive
**Area:** Rathgar
**Address:** 93 Ranelagh Village Dublin 6
**Phone:** 353 1 4975577

#246
**Oliveto Osteria**
**Cuisines:** Italian
**Average price:** Expensive
**Area:** Dún Laoghaire
**Address:** 9-12 Haddington Ter Dublin
**Phone:** 353 1 2800011

#247
**Ten Fourteen**
**Cuisines:** Seafood
**Average price:** Modest
**Area:** Clontarf
**Address:** 324 Clontarf Rd Dublin 3
**Phone:** 353 1 8054877

#248
**Metro Cafe**
**Cuisines:** Cafe
**Average price:** Inexpensive
**Area:** South Inner City
**Address:** 43 S William St Dublin 2
**Phone:** 353 1 6794515

#249
**Woodstock Café**
**Cuisines:** Cafe
**Average price:** Modest
**Area:** BRdstone
**Address:** 156 Phibsboro Rd Dublin 7
**Phone:** 353 1 8300265

#250
**Fish Shop**
**Cuisines:** Fish & Chips
**Average price:** Modest
**Area:** Blackrock
**Address:** 16 George's Place Dublin
**Phone:** 353 85 7041542

#251
**Kilkenny Restaurant**
**Cuisines:** Breakfast & Brunch,
Sandwiches, Coffee & Tea
**Average price:** Inexpensive
**Area:** South Inner City
**Address:** 6 Nassau St Dublin 2
**Phone:** 353 1 6777075

#252
**The Woollen Mills**
**Cuisines:** Irish
**Average price:** Modest
**Area:** North Inner City
**Address:** 41/42 Lower Ormond
Quay Dublin 1
**Phone:** 353 1 8728035

#253
**Kingfisher**
**Cuisines:** Guest Houses,
Breakfast & Brunch
**Average price:** Modest
**Area:** North Inner City
**Address:** 166-168 Parnell St Dublin 1
**Phone:** 353 1 8728732

#254
**Base Wood Fired Pizza**
**Cuisines:** Pizza
**Average price:** Expensive
**Area:** Terenure
**Address:** 92 Terenure Rd East Dublin 6
**Phone:** 353 1 4404800

#255
**Harrys Kitchen Restaurant**
**Cuisines:** Bistro
**Average price:** Modest
**Area:** South Inner City
**Address:** 22 Dawson St Dublin 2
**Phone:** 353 1 6394889

#256
**Ananda Restaurant**
**Cuisines:** Indian
**Average price:** Expensive
**Area:** Sandyford
**Address:** Sandyford Rd Dublin 14
**Phone:** 353 1 2960099

#257
**Dax Restaurant**
**Cuisines:** French
**Average price:** Exclusive
**Area:** South Inner City
**Address:** 23 Upper Pembroke St Dublin 2
**Phone:** 353 1 6761494

#258
**Belluccis Italian Restaurant**
**Cuisines:** Pizza, Italian
**Average price:** Modest
**Area:** Ballsbridge
**Address:** 22-30 Merrion Rd Dublin 4
**Phone:** 353 1 6689422

#259
**Beshoffs of Howth**
**Cuisines:** Seafood, Seafood Market
**Average price:** Modest
**Area:** Howth
**Address:** 17/18 West Pier Dublin 13
**Phone:** 353 1 8390766

#260
**Falafel & Kebab**
**Cuisines:** Kebab, Halal, Vegetarian
**Average price:** Modest
**Area:** Temple Bar
**Address:** 11 Essex St East Dublin 2
**Phone:** 353 1 6730000

#261
**Dillingers**
**Cuisines:** American, Breakfast & Brunch
**Average price:** Modest
**Area:** Rathgar
**Address:** 47 Ranelagh Village Dublin 6
**Phone:** 353 1 4978010

#262
**Deli-Suz**
**Cuisines:** Deli, Coffee & Tea
**Average price:** Inexpensive
**Area:** Inns Quay
**Address:** Blessington St Dublin 7
**Phone:** 353 1 8603871

#263
**Tolteca**
**Cuisines:** Mexican
**Average price:** Modest
**Area:** Baggot St
**Address:** 38 Upper Baggot St Dublin 4
**Phone:** 353 1 6688604

#264
**Cafe Oasis**
**Cuisines:** Cafe, Mediterranean,
Fast Food
**Average price:** Inexpensive
**Area:** Smithfield
**Address:** 54 North King St Dublin 7
**Phone:** 353 1 8740070

#265
**Brasserie Sixty6**
**Cuisines:** Brasserie, European,
Breakfast & Brunch
**Average price:** Expensive
**Area:** South Inner City
**Address:** 66-67 S Great Georges St Dublin 2
**Phone:** 353 1 4005878

#266
**TP Smiths**
**Cuisines:** Pub, European, Gastropub
**Average price:** Modest
**Area:** North Inner City
**Address:** 9-10 Jervis St Dublin 1
**Phone:** 353 1 8724031

#267
**The Copper Bar**
**Cuisines:** Bar, Steakhouse
**Average price:** Expensive
**Area:** Sandyford
**Address:** 8 Blackthorne Rd Dublin 18
**Phone:** 353 1 2052033

#268
**Trocadero Restaurant**
**Cuisines:** Steakhouse, European
**Average price:** Expensive
**Area:** Lucan
**Address:** 3 St Andrews St Dublin 2
**Phone:** 353 1 6775545

#269
**Burritos & Blues**
**Cuisines:** Mexican, Fast Food
**Average price:** Modest
**Area:** South Inner City
**Address:** 28 South Anne St Dublin 2
**Phone:** 353 86 3000500

#270
**Blue Orchid**
**Cuisines:** Thai
**Average price:** Modest
**Area:** Blackrock
**Address:** Newpark Center Dublin
**Phone:** 353 1 2831767

#271
**Mezza**
**Cuisines:** Fast Food, Middle Eastern
**Average price:** Modest
**Area:** Temple Bar
**Address:** 13 Parliament St Dublin 2
**Phone:** 353 1 6706424

#272
**Mourne Seafood Bar**
**Cuisines:** Seafood, Bar
**Average price:** Expensive
**Area:** Grand Canal Dock
**Address:** Charlotte Quay Dublin
**Phone:** 353 1 6688862

#273
**Café Novo**
**Cuisines:** Brasserie, Cafe
**Average price:** Expensive
**Area:** South Inner City
**Address:** Harry St Dublin 2
**Phone:** 353 1 6463353

#274
**Havana**
**Cuisines:** Spanish, Tapas Bar
**Average price:** Modest
**Area:** South Inner City
**Address:** South Great George's St Dublin 2
**Phone:** 353 1 4005990

#275
**Stillorgan Orchard**
**Cuisines:** Gastropub, Music Venues
**Average price:** Modest
**Area:** Stillorgan
**Address:** 1 The Hill Dublin
**Phone:** 353 1 2886793

#276
**Camden Rotisserie**
**Cuisines:** Barbeque, Diner
**Average price:** Modest
**Area:** Harcourt
**Address:** 37 Camden St Lower Dublin 2
**Phone:** 353 1 5381022

#277
**Las Tapas**
**Cuisines:** Tapas Bar, Spanish
**Average price:** Modest
**Area:** Cabinteely
**Address:** 8 old bray Rd Dublin 18
**Phone:** 353 1 2369869

#278
**Jewel in the Crown**
**Cuisines:** Indian
**Average price:** Modest
**Area:** Ballsbridge
**Address:** 41-43 Shelbourne Rd Dublin 4
**Phone:** 353 1 6670959

#279
**Bistro Spice**
**Cuisines:** Indian
**Average price:** Modest
**Area:** Monkstown
**Address:** 101 Monkstown Rd Dublin
**Phone:** 353 1 2304555

#280
**Seven Social**
**Cuisines:** American, Irish, Brasserie
**Average price:** Modest
**Area:** Smithfield
**Address:** 76 Benburb St Dublin 7
**Phone:** 353 1 6729080

#281
**The Lobster Pot Restaurant**
**Cuisines:** Seafood
**Average price:** Exclusive
**Area:** Ballsbridge
**Address:** 9 Ballsbridge Ter Dublin 4
**Phone:** 353 1 6680025

#282
**Tramyard Cafe**
**Cuisines:** Coffee & Tea,
Breakfast & Brunch
**Average price:** Modest
**Area:** Dalkey
**Address:** Castle St Dublin
**Phone:** 353 87 2551261

#283
**Milano**
**Cuisines:** Italian
**Average price:** Modest
**Area:** Grand Canal Dock
**Address:** Unit 1 - Hanover Quay Dublin 2
**Phone:** 353 1 6799579

#284
**The Pavillion**
**Cuisines:** Bar, Gastropub
**Average price:** Inexpensive
**Area:** South Inner City
**Address:** Trinity College Dublin 2
**Phone:** 353 1 6081279

#285
**Cinnamon**
**Cuisines:** Breakfast & Brunch,
Cafe, Gluten-Free
**Average price:** Modest
**Area:** Rathgar
**Address:** 83/87 Ranelagh Dublin 6
**Phone:** 353 1 9013020

#286
**Bar Italia**
**Cuisines:** Italian, Pizza
**Average price:** Modest
**Area:** North Inner City
**Address:** 26 Lower Ormond Quay
Dublin 1
**Phone:** 353 1 8741000

#287
**Damson Diner**
**Cuisines:** American, Asian Fusion
**Average price:** Modest
**Area:** South Inner City
**Address:** 52 South William St Dublin 2
**Phone:** 353 1 6777007

#288
**Enoteca Torino**
**Cuisines:** Italian
**Average price:** Modest
**Area:** Inchicore
**Address:** 9 Grattan Crescent Dublin 8
**Phone:** 353 1 4537791

#289
**The Bailey**
**Cuisines:** Pub, Gastropub
**Average price:** Modest
**Area:** South Inner City
**Address:** Duke St Dublin 2
**Phone:** 353 1 6704939

#290
**Good World Restaurant**
**Cuisines:** Chinese
**Average price:** Modest
**Area:** South Inner City
**Address:** 18 South Great
George's St Dublin 2
**Phone:** 353 1 6775373

#291
**Avoca Food Market & Salt Café**
**Cuisines:** Cafe, Grocery
**Average price:** Modest
**Area:** Dún Laoghaire
**Address:** The Crescent, Monkstown
**Phone:** 353 1 2020230

#292
**Kanum**
**Cuisines:** Thai
**Average price:** Modest
**Area:** Baggot St
**Address:** 77 Mespil Rd Dublin 4
**Phone:** 353 1 6608616

#293
**Sultan Restaurant**
**Cuisines:** Halal, Middle Eastern
**Average price:** Inexpensive
**Area:** South Inner City
**Address:** 73 S Great Georges St Dublin 2
**Phone:** 353 1 4788077

#294
**The Big Blue Bus**
**Cuisines:** Pizza
**Average price:** Inexpensive
**Area:** Harcourt
**Address:** 12 S Richmond St Dublin 2
**Phone:** 353 86 0559935

#295
**One Pico**
**Cuisines:** French
**Average price:** Exclusive
**Area:** South Inner City
**Address:** 5-6 Molesworth Place Dublin 2
**Phone:** 353 1 6760300

#296
**Okayu**
**Cuisines:** Japanese
**Average price:** Modest
**Area:** Ballybough
**Address:** 71 N Strand Rd Dublin 3
**Phone:** 353 1 8194741

#297
**Viva**
**Cuisines:** Spanish, Tapas Bar,
Gluten-Free
**Average price:** Modest
**Area:** Harcourt
**Address:** 27 South Richmond St Dublin 2
**Phone:** 353 1 4244043

#298
**Brick Alley Cafe**
**Cuisines:** Cafe
**Average price:** Modest
**Area:** Temple Bar
**Address:** 25 E Essex St Dublin 2
**Phone:** 353 1 6793393

#299
**New Millenium**
**Cuisines:** Chinese
**Average price:** Expensive
**Area:** South Inner City
**Address:** 51 S King St Dublin 2
**Phone:** 353 1 6351525

#300
**Tamp & Stitch**
**Cuisines:** Jewelry, Coffee & Tea
**Average price:** Modest
**Area:** Temple Bar
**Address:** Unit 3 Scarlet Row Dublin 8
**Phone:** 353 1 5154705

#301
**The Black Apple Café**
**Cuisines:** Breakfast & Brunch,
Coffee & Tea
**Average price:** Inexpensive
**Area:** Harold's Cross
**Address:** 208 Harolds Cross Rd
Dublin 6w
**Phone:** 353 1 4978632

#302
**Peacock Green**
**Cuisines:** Cafe, Deli
**Average price:** Modest
**Area:** Harcourt
**Address:** Hatch St Upper Dublin 2
**Phone:** 353 1 4112946

#303
**JD's Steakhouse**
**Cuisines:** Steakhouse
**Average price:** Expensive
**Area:** Terenure
**Address:** 4 Rathfarnham Rd Dublin 6
**Phone:** 353 1 4925812

#304
**Amir's Delights**
**Cuisines:** Turkish
**Average price:** Inexpensive
**Area:** Temple Bar
**Address:** 5 Blooms Lane Dublin 1
**Phone:** 353 86 3536404

#305
**Keoghs Café**
**Cuisines:** Coffee & Tea, Sandwiches
**Average price:** Modest
**Area:** South Inner City
**Address:** 1-2 Trinity St Dublin 2
**Phone:** 353 1 6778599

#306
**Mario's Restaurant**
**Cuisines:** Italian
**Average price:** Modest
**Area:** Rathgar
**Address:** 37/39 Ranelagh Village
Dublin 6
**Phone:** 353 1 4972078

#307
**Pacinos**
**Cuisines:** Italian, Dance Club
**Average price:** Modest
**Area:** South Inner City
**Address:** 18 Suffolk St Dublin 2
**Phone:** 353 1 6775651

#308
**Michie Sushi**
**Cuisines:** Sushi Bar
**Average price:** Modest
**Area:** Sandyford
**Address:** Unit B1, R3, Beacon
South Quarter Dublin
**Phone:** 44 1555 0174

#309
**O'Briens**
**Cuisines:** Coffee & Tea, Sandwiches
**Average price:** Inexpensive
**Area:** IFSC
**Address:** 3 Georges Dock Dublin 1
**Phone:** 353 1 6701900

#310
**Cobalt Cafe & Gallery**
**Cuisines:** Coffee & Tea
**Average price:** Modest
**Area:** Rotunda
**Address:** 16 N Great Georges St Dublin 1
**Phone:** 353 1 8730313

#311
**Brownes Steakhouse**
**Cuisines:** Steakhouse
**Average price:** Exclusive
**Area:** Blanchardstown
**Address:** Main St Dublin 15
**Phone:** 353 1 8221551

#312
**Jimmy Chungs**
**Cuisines:** Chinese
**Average price:** Modest
**Area:** North Inner City
**Address:** 8 Eden Quay Dublin 1
**Phone:** 353 1 8740888

#313
**Alfie's Restaurant**
**Cuisines:** European, Bar
**Average price:** Modest
**Area:** South Inner City
**Address:** 10 S William St Dublin 2
**Phone:** 353 1 6718767

#314
**The Harbourmaster**
**Cuisines:** Pub, European
**Average price:** Modest
**Area:** IFSC
**Address:** Customs House Dock Dublin 1
**Phone:** 353 1 6701553

#315
**Hugos**
**Cuisines:** French, Bistro
**Average price:** Expensive
**Area:** South Inner City
**Address:** 6 Merrion Row Dublin 2
**Phone:** 353 1 6765955

#316
**The Table**
**Cuisines:** Irish
**Average price:** Expensive
**Area:** Harcourt
**Address:** Portobello Rd Dublin 8
**Phone:** 353 1 4736727

#317
**Cafe du Journal**
**Cuisines:** Breakfast & Brunch,
Coffee & Tea
**Average price:** Modest
**Area:** Dún Laoghaire
**Address:** 17A The Crescent Dublin
**Phone:** 353 1 2143854

#318
**Foley's Bar**
**Cuisines:** Pub, Irish
**Average price:** Modest
**Area:** South Inner City
**Address:** 1 Merrion Row Dublin 2
**Phone:** 353 1 6610140

#319
**Taste Food Company
Cafe and Bistro**
**Cuisines:** Coffee & Tea, Bistro,
Breakfast & Brunch
**Average price:** Modest
**Area:** South Inner City
**Address:** 39/40 S William St Dublin 2
**Phone:** 353 1 6798475

#320
**Irish Film Institute**
**Cuisines:** Cinema, Cafe
**Average price:** Modest
**Area:** Temple Bar
**Address:** 6 Eustace St Dublin 2
**Phone:** 353 1 6795744

#321
**Vincenzo's Pizzeria**
**Cuisines:** Pizza, Italian, Fast Food
**Average price:** Modest
**Area:** The Liberties
**Address:** 54A Thomas St Dublin 8
**Phone:** 353 1 4533032

#322
**Moloughney's**
**Cuisines:** American, Irish
**Average price:** Modest
**Area:** Clontarf
**Address:** 9 Vernon Avenue Dublin 3
**Phone:** 353 1 8330002

#323
**Mannings Bakery & Café**
**Cuisines:** Coffee & Tea, Bakery,
Breakfast & Brunch
**Average price:** Inexpensive
**Area:** The Liberties
**Address:** 40 Thomas St Dublin 8
**Phone:** 353 1 4542114

#324
**Wings Gourmet Burger**
**Cuisines:** Burgers
**Average price:** Inexpensive
**Area:** North Inner City
**Address:** Upper O'Connell St Dublin 1
**Phone:** 353 87 3608040

#325
**Picasso Restaurant**
**Cuisines:** Irish, Italian
**Average price:** Expensive
**Area:** Clontarf
**Address:** 1 Vernon Avenue Dublin 3
**Phone:** 353 1 8531120

#326
**Market Canteen**
**Cuisines:** Bistro
**Average price:** Modest
**Area:** Blackrock
**Address:** 19a Main St Dublin
**Phone:** 353 85 1836700

#327
**Ambala**
**Cuisines:** Desserts, Pakistani, Indian
**Average price:** Modest
**Area:** Harcourt
**Address:** 11 Upper Camden St Dublin 2
**Phone:** 353 1 4759094

#328
**Delhi O'Deli**
**Cuisines:** Indian, Vegetarian
**Average price:** Inexpensive
**Area:** North Inner City
**Address:** 12 Moore St Dublin 1
**Phone:** 353 1 8729129

#329
**Stir Crazy**
**Cuisines:** Asian Fusion
**Average price:** Inexpensive
**Area:** South Inner City
**Address:** 63 Dame St Dublin 2
**Phone:** 353 1 6722200

#330
**Grand Central Cafe Bar**
**Cuisines:** Gastropub, Pub, Steakhouse
**Average price:** Modest
**Area:** North Inner City
**Address:** 10-11 Lower O'Connell St
**Phone:** 353 1 8728658

#331
**Saint**
**Cuisines:** Irish
**Average price:** Modest
**Area:** South Inner City
**Address:** 7 Saint Andrew St Dublin 2
**Phone:** 353 1 4853273

#332
**The Gables/McCabes Wines**
**Cuisines:** Bar, Mediterranean
**Average price:** Expensive
**Area:** Foxrock
**Address:** Torquay Rd Dublin 18
**Phone:** 353 1 2892174

#333
**Bewley's Cafe**
**Cuisines:** Coffee & Tea, Irish, Cafe
**Average price:** Modest
**Area:** South Inner City
**Address:** 78-79 Grafton St Dublin 2
**Phone:** 353 1 6727720

#334
**El Bahia**
**Cuisines:** Moroccan, Middle Eastern
**Average price:** Modest
**Area:** South Inner City
**Address:** 37 Wicklow St Dublin 2
**Phone:** 353 1 6770213

#335
**The Italian Corner**
**Cuisines:** Italian
**Average price:** Modest
**Area:** Temple Bar
**Address:** 23/24 Wellington Quay Dublin 2
**Phone:** 353 1 6719114

#336
**Pink Elephant Thai Retaurant**
**Cuisines:** Thai
**Average price:** Modest
**Area:** Finglas
**Address:** Main Court Dublin
**Phone:** 353 1 8904233

#337
**Ocha Teppanyaki & Sushi Bar**
**Cuisines:** Japanese, Thai
**Average price:** Expensive
**Area:** Dundrum
**Address:** 2 Main St Dublin 14
**Phone:** 353 1 5372963

#338
**Canters**
**Cuisines:** Irish, Indian
**Average price:** Exclusive
**Area:** Marino
**Address:** 9 Fairview Strand Dublin 3
**Phone:** 353 1 8333681

#339
**Embassy Grill**
**Cuisines:** Fast Food
**Average price:** Inexpensive
**Area:** Ballsbridge
**Address:** 172 Pembroke Rd Dublin 4
**Phone:** 353 1 6600841

#340
**Yamamori Noodles**
**Cuisines:** Sushi Bar, Japanese
**Average price:** Modest
**Area:** South Inner City
**Address:** 71 - 72 South Great
George's St Dublin 2
**Phone:** 353 1 4755001

#341
**McHugh's Wine & Dine Restaurant**
**Cuisines:** Irish, European
**Average price:** Expensive
**Area:** Raheny
**Address:** 59 St Assams Park Dublin 5
**Phone:** 353 1 8327435

#342
**Unicorn Italian**
**Restaurant & Cafe**
**Cuisines:** European, Italian, Deli
**Average price:** Expensive
**Area:** South Inner City
**Address:** 12b Merrion Court Dublin 2
**Phone:** 353 1 6624757

#343
**Chili Club**
**Cuisines:** Thai
**Average price:** Expensive
**Area:** South Inner City
**Address:** 1 Anne's Ln Dublin 2
**Phone:** 353 1 6773721

#344
**The Cliff Townhouse**
**Cuisines:** Irish, Seafood
**Average price:** Exclusive
**Area:** South Inner City
**Address:** 22 St. Stephens Green Dublin 2
**Phone:** 353 1 6383939

#345
**Presto**
**Cuisines:** Fish & Chips
**Average price:** Inexpensive
**Area:** Beggars Bush
**Address:** 8 South Lotts Rd Dublin 4
**Phone:** 353 1 6680392

#346
**Zaragoza Dublin**
**Cuisines:** Spanish
**Average price:** Modest
**Area:** South Inner City
**Address:** 18 South William St Dublin 2
**Phone:** 353 1 6794020

#347
**Dublin City Food**
**Cuisines:** Sandwiches, Cafe, Irish
**Average price:** Modest
**Area:** South Inner City
**Address:** 7 Saint Andrews St Dublin 2
**Phone:** 353 1 4853273

#348
**The Food Room**
**Cuisines:** Deli, Coffee & Tea, Sandwiches
**Average price:** Inexpensive
**Area:** Clontarf
**Address:** 46 Clontarf Rd Dublin 3
**Phone:** 353 1 8332259

#349
**Dada Restaurant**
**Cuisines:** Moroccan, Middle Eastern
**Average price:** Expensive
**Area:** South Inner City
**Address:** 45 South William St Dublin 2
**Phone:** 353 1 6170777

#350
**Wagamama**
**Cuisines:** Japanese
**Average price:** Modest
**Area:** Blanchardstown
**Address:** Blanchardstown Retail Park 2
**Phone:** 353 1 8219449

#351
**Dobbins**
**Cuisines:** European
**Average price:** Expensive
**Area:** Baggot St
**Address:** 15 Stephens Lane Dublin 2
**Phone:** 353 1 6764679

#352
**Tamara Thai &**
**Malaysian Restaurant**
**Cuisines:** Thai
**Average price:** Modest
**Area:** Tallaght
**Address:** Belgard Square Dublin
**Phone:** 353 1 4140888

#353
**Il Fornaio**
**Cuisines:** Italian
**Average price:** Modest
**Area:** IFSC
**Address:** 1B Valentia House Dublin 1
**Phone:** 353 1 6721852

#354
**The Gasworks Bar**
**Cuisines:** Pub, Gastropub
**Average price:** Modest
**Area:** Grand Canal Dock
**Address:** Grand Canal St Dublin 4
**Phone:** 353 1 6461000

#355
**Da Mimmo**
**Cuisines:** Italian, Food Delivery Services
**Average price:** Modest
**Area:** North Strand
**Address:** 148 North Strand Dublin 3
**Phone:** 353 1 8561714

#356
**Aussie BBQ**
**Cuisines:** Barbeque, Burgers
**Average price:** Modest
**Area:** Harcourt
**Address:** 5 S Richmond St Dublin 2
**Phone:** 353 1 4789125

#357
**La Cave Winebar & Restaurant**
**Cuisines:** Steakhouse, Wine Bar, French
**Average price:** Expensive
**Area:** South Inner City
**Address:** 28 South Anne St Dublin 2
**Phone:** 353 1 6794409

#358
**Lovin Catering**
**Cuisines:** Caterers, Coffee & Tea,
Sandwiches
**Average price:** Modest
**Area:** The Liberties
**Address:** 49 Francis St Dublin 8
**Phone:** 353 1 4544912

#359
**Shangri-La**
**Cuisines:** Malaysian, Chinese
**Average price:** Modest
**Area:** Stoneybatter
**Address:** 16 Stoneybatter Dublin 7
**Phone:** 353 1 6725002

#360
**Il Fico**
**Cuisines:** Italian
**Average price:** Modest
**Area:** South Inner City
**Address:** Chatham St Dublin 2
**Phone:** 353 1 6799124

#361
**TOSS'D Noodles & Salads**
**Cuisines:** Thai, Asian Fusion
**Average price:** Modest
**Area:** IFSC
**Address:** CHQ Building Dublin 1
**Phone:** 353 1 8291607

#362
**Noshington Cafe**
**Cuisines:** Breakfast & Brunch, Irish
**Average price:** Modest
**Area:** South Circular Rd
**Address:** 186 S Circular Rd Dublin 8
**Phone:** 353 1 4100414

#363
**Cafe Libro**
**Cuisines:** Cafe
**Average price:** Inexpensive
**Area:** Dundrum
**Address:** Tesco Car Park Dublin 16
**Phone:** 353 1 2966196

#364
**Hemingways Deli**
**Cuisines:** Deli
**Average price:** Inexpensive
**Area:** Ballsbridge
**Address:** 2A Merrion Rd Dublin 4
**Phone:** 353 1 6689950

#365
### Science Gallery Dublin Café
**Cuisines:** Coffee & Tea, Pizza, Cafe
**Average price:** Modest
**Area:** South Inner City
**Address:** Pearse St Dublin 2
**Phone:** 353 1 8964138

#366
### Chameleon
**Cuisines:** Indonesian, Asian Fusion
**Average price:** Expensive
**Area:** South Inner City
**Address:** 1 Lower Fownes St Dublin 2
**Phone:** 353 1 6710362

#367
### Dave's Wood-Fired Pizza Co.
**Cuisines:** Pizza, Food Stand
**Average price:** Modest
**Area:** South Inner City
**Address:** Dublin 2
**Phone:** 353 86 7724744

#368
### Mes Amis
**Cuisines:** Cafe
**Average price:** Inexpensive
**Area:** North Inner City
**Address:** 37 Upper Abbey St Dublin 1
**Phone:** 353 1 8729963

#369
### Angel Park Eatery
**Cuisines:** American
**Average price:** Modest
**Area:** Baggot St
**Address:** 5 Lower Mount St Dublin 2
**Phone:** 353 1 6763010

#370
### Toni's
**Cuisines:** Fast Food
**Average price:** Inexpensive
**Area:** Kilmainham
**Address:** 95 Emmet Rd Dublin 8
**Phone:** 353 1 4730701

#371
### Roast
**Cuisines:** Irish
**Average price:** Expensive
**Area:** Ballsbridge
**Address:** 10 Merrion Rd Dublin 4
**Phone:** 353 1 6144727

#372
### KC Peaches
**Cuisines:** Deli
**Average price:** Modest
**Area:** Grand Canal Dock
**Address:** Pearse St Dublin 2
**Phone:** 353 1 6770333

#373
### Quigleys Cafe
**Cuisines:** Cafe
**Average price:** Inexpensive
**Area:** North Inner City
**Address:** Henry St Dublin 1
**Phone:** 353 1 8733973

#374
### Pepperpot Cafe
**Cuisines:** Coffee & Tea,
Breakfast & Brunch, Gluten-Free
**Average price:** Modest
**Area:** South Inner City
**Address:** South William St Dublin 2
**Phone:** 353 1 7071610

#375
### BRdway Pizza Parlour
**Cuisines:** Pizza
**Average price:** Modest
**Area:** IFSC
**Address:** Custom House Square
IFSC Dublin 1
**Phone:** 353 1 6721812

#376
### Solas Bar & Restaurant
**Cuisines:** Gastropub, Bar
**Average price:** Modest
**Area:** South Inner City
**Address:** 31 Wexford St Dublin 2
**Phone:** 353 1 4780583

#377
### Shack Restaurant
**Cuisines:** Irish
**Average price:** Modest
**Area:** Temple Bar
**Address:** 24 East Essex St Dublin 2
**Phone:** 353 1 6790043

#378
### The Gotham Café
**Cuisines:** American, Pizza, Cafe
**Average price:** Modest
**Area:** South Inner City
**Address:** 8 S Anne St Dublin 2
**Phone:** 353 1 6795266

#379
**Gourmet Burger Kitchen**
**Cuisines:** American
**Average price:** Modest
**Area:** South Inner City
**Address:** 5 South Anne St Dublin 2
**Phone:** 353 1 6728559

#380
**Captain America's**
**Cuisines:** Steakhouse, Burgers
**Average price:** Modest
**Area:** South Inner City
**Address:** 44 Grafton St Dublin 2
**Phone:** 353 1 6715266

#381
**Peacock Green**
**Cuisines:** Cafe, Bistro, Brasserie
**Average price:** Inexpensive
**Area:** South Inner City
**Address:** 13 Lord Edward St Dublin 2
**Phone:** 353 1 4758800

#382
**Frite Haus**
**Cuisines:** Hot Dogs, German, Belgian
**Average price:** Modest
**Area:** Harcourt
**Address:** 87 Camden St Dublin 2
**Phone:** 353 87 0505964

#383
**Ming Court Chinese Restaurant**
**Cuisines:** Dim Sum
**Average price:** Modest
**Area:** Blanchardstown
**Address:** Unit 453 Blanchardstown
Centre Dublin 15
**Phone:** 353 1 8243388

#384
**Millers Pizza Kitchen**
**Cuisines:** Pizza
**Average price:** Modest
**Area:** Baggot St
**Address:** 50 Upper Baggot St Dublin 4
**Phone:** 353 1 6606022

#385
**Sab Inn Cafe**
**Cuisines:** Hungarian, Diner
**Average price:** Modest
**Area:** Bolton St
**Address:** 61 Bolton St Dublin 1
**Phone:** 353 1 8733810

#386
**Castello Bruno**
**Cuisines:** Italian
**Average price:** Expensive
**Area:** Castleknock
**Address:** Main St Dublin 5
**Phone:** 353 1 8228400

#387
**Brewbaker**
**Cuisines:** Deli, Cafe, Sandwiches
**Average price:** Inexpensive
**Area:** Rotunda
**Address:** 22 S Frederick St Dublin 2
**Phone:** 353 1 6778288

#388
**Brasserie le Pont**
**Cuisines:** Brasserie, French
**Average price:** Expensive
**Area:** Baggot St
**Address:** 26 Fitzwilliam Place Dublin 2
**Phone:** 353 1 6694600

#389
**Bella Cuba**
**Cuisines:** Latin American
**Average price:** Modest
**Area:** Ballsbridge
**Address:** 11 Ballsbridge Ter Dublin 4
**Phone:** 353 1 6605539

#390
**Merrion Inn**
**Cuisines:** Pub, Gastropub
**Average price:** Modest
**Area:** Merrion
**Address:** 188 Merrion Rd Dublin 4
**Phone:** 353 1 2693816

#391
**Red Rose Café**
**Cuisines:** Coffee & Tea
**Average price:** Modest
**Area:** South Inner City
**Address:** 23 Dawson St Dublin 2
**Phone:** 353 86 3704873

#392
**Douglas and Kaldi**
**Cuisines:** Breakfast & Brunch, Sandwiches
**Average price:** Modest
**Area:** Navan Rd
**Address:** Unit 15 Ashtown Square Dublin 15
**Phone:** 353 1 8996465

#393
**Stage Door Café**
**Cuisines:** Coffee & Tea,
Breakfast & Brunch
**Average price:** Modest
**Area:** Temple Bar
**Address:** 11-12 E Essex St Dublin 2
**Phone:** 353 1 8735162

#394
**Beshoff Restaurant**
**Cuisines:** Fish & Chips
**Average price:** Modest
**Area:** North Inner City
**Address:** 6 Upper O'Connell St Dublin 1
**Phone:** 353 1 8724400

#395
**Howards Way Cafe**
**Cuisines:** Coffee & Tea, Brasserie
**Average price:** Modest
**Area:** Terenure
**Address:** 8 Orwell Rd Dublin 6
**Phone:** 353 1 4967821

#396
**La Caverna**
**Cuisines:** Italian, Wine Bar, Steakhouse
**Average price:** Expensive
**Area:** Temple Bar
**Address:** 12 Fownes St Dublin 2
**Phone:** 353 1 6703110

#397
**South St Restaurant**
**Cuisines:** Restaurant
**Average price:** Modest
**Area:** South Inner City
**Address:** S Great George's St Dublin 2
**Phone:** 353 1 4752273

#398
**Sakura Sushi**
**Cuisines:** Japanese, Sushi Bar, Fast Food
**Average price:** Inexpensive
**Area:** Harold's Cross
**Address:** 157 Lower Kimmage Rd Dublin 6w
**Phone:** 353 1 5558888

#399
**Taste of Brazil**
**Cuisines:** Brazilian
**Average price:** Modest
**Area:** Temple Bar
**Address:** 32 Parliament St Dublin ?
**Phone:** 053 1 8759973

#400
**Worscht-Gourmet Sausages**
**Cuisines:** Irish, Fast Food
**Average price:** Modest
**Area:** South Inner City
**Address:** Georges St Arcade Dublin 2
**Phone:** 353 87 2536261

#401
**Poulet Bonne Femme**
**Cuisines:** Specialty Food, Sandwiches
**Average price:** Inexpensive
**Area:** South Inner City
**Address:** 13 Suffolk St Dublin 2
**Phone:** 353 1 6774215

#402
**Overends**
**Cuisines:** Irish, Cafe
**Average price:** Modest
**Area:** Dundrum
**Address:** Overend Way Dublin 14
**Phone:** 353 1 9696666

#403
**Boulevard Café**
**Cuisines:** Cafe
**Average price:** Modest
**Area:** South Inner City
**Address:** 27 Exchequer St Dublin 2
**Phone:** 353 1 6792131

#404
**Voilà**
**Cuisines:** Breakfast & Brunch, Cafe
**Average price:** Modest
**Area:** South Inner City
**Address:** 14 Lower Baggot St Dublin 2
**Phone:** 353 1 6629353

#405
**Old Punch Bowl**
**Cuisines:** Pub, Gastropub
**Average price:** Modest
**Area:** Booterstown
**Address:** 116 Rock Rd Dublin
**Phone:** 353 1 2832356

#406
**Gerry's Coffee Shop**
**Cuisines:** Breakfast & Brunch, Diner
**Average price:** Inexpensive
**Area:** South Inner City
**Address:** 6 Montague St Dublin 2
**Phone:** 353 1 4783524

#407
**Nando's**
**Cuisines:** Portuguese
**Average price:** Modest
**Area:** North Inner City
**Address:** 51-2 Mary St Dublin 1
**Phone:** 353 1 8720011

#408
**Sherie's Café Bar**
**Cuisines:** Irish, Sandwiches, Cafe
**Average price:** Modest
**Area:** North Inner City
**Address:** 3 Lower Abbey St Dublin 1
**Phone:** 353 1 8747237

#409
**Eden Bar and Grill**
**Cuisines:** Wine Bar, Barbeque
**Average price:** Expensive
**Area:** South Inner City
**Address:** 7 South William St Dublin 2
**Phone:** 353 1 6706887

#410
**Lolly and Cooks**
**Cuisines:** Coffee & Tea,
Breakfast & Brunch
**Average price:** Modest
**Area:** Grand Canal Dock
**Address:** 2 Forbes St Dublin 2
**Phone:** 353 1 6798442

#411
**Al Boschetto**
**Cuisines:** Italian, Fast Food
**Average price:** Modest
**Area:** Ballsbridge
**Address:** 2 Merrion Rd Dublin 4
**Phone:** 353 1 6673784

#412
**The Mercantile Bar**
**Cuisines:** Pub, Irish
**Average price:** Modest
**Area:** South Inner City
**Address:** 28 Dame St Dublin 2
**Phone:** 353 1 6707100

#413
**Geisha**
**Cuisines:** Asian Fusion, Japanese, Thai
**Average price:** Expensive
**Area:** Navan Rd
**Address:** 73-74 Ashtown Village Dublin 15
**Phone:** 353 1 8664959

#414
**Dicey Reilly's**
**Cuisines:** Bar, Gastropub, Dance Club
**Average price:** Inexpensive
**Area:** Harcourt
**Address:** 21-25 Harcourt St Dublin 2
**Phone:** 353 1 4784841

#415
**The Ritz Cafe**
**Cuisines:** Fish & Chips
**Average price:** Inexpensive
**Area:** Dún Laoghaire
**Address:** Patrick St Dublin
**Phone:** 353 1 2300002

#416
**Toast Cafe Bar**
**Cuisines:** European, Sports Bar
**Average price:** Modest
**Area:** Rathmines
**Address:** 196 Rathmines Rd
Lower Dublin 6
**Phone:** 353 1 4126285

#417
**Gourmet Burger Kitchen**
**Cuisines:** Burgers
**Average price:** Modest
**Area:** Temple Bar
**Address:** Temple Bar Square Dublin 2
**Phone:** 353 1 6708343

#418
**Gallaher & Co Bistro**
**& Coffee House**
**Cuisines:** European
**Average price:** Modest
**Area:** South Inner City
**Address:** 16A D'Olier St Dublin 2
**Phone:** 353 1 6770499

#419
**Town Bar and Grill**
**Cuisines:** Italian, European, Irish
**Average price:** Expensive
**Area:** South Inner City
**Address:** 21 Kildare St Dublin 2
**Phone:** 353 1 6624724

#420
**Mandarin Castle**
**Cuisines:** Fast Food, Chinese
**Average price:** Modest
**Area:** Castleknock
**Address:** Unit 10 Castleknock Village
Centre Dublin 15
**Phone:** 353 1 8204843

#421
**Caffe Noto**
**Cuisines:** Coffee & Tea,
Sandwiches, Bagels
**Average price:** Inexpensive
**Area:** The Liberties
**Address:** 79 Thomas St Dublin 8
**Phone:** 353 1 4547223

#422
**Darkey Kellys**
**Cuisines:** Pub, Irish
**Average price:** Inexpensive
**Area:** Wood Quay
**Address:** Copper Alley, Fishamble St
Dublin 8
**Phone:** 353 1 6796500

#423
**Grove Rd**
**Cuisines:** Cafe, Breakfast & Brunch
**Average price:** Inexpensive
**Area:** Rathmines
**Address:** 1 Lower Rathmines Rd Dublin 6
**Phone:** 353 1 5446639

#424
**Sushi King**
**Cuisines:** Sushi Bar, Japanese
**Average price:** Modest
**Area:** South Inner City
**Address:** 146 Baggot St Lower Dublin 2
**Phone:** 353 1 6449836

#425
**Ka Shing**
**Cuisines:** Szechuan, Dim Sum
**Average price:** Modest
**Area:** South Inner City
**Address:** 12A Wicklow St Dublin 2
**Phone:** 353 1 6772580

#426
**Patrick's Cafe**
**Cuisines:** Breakfast & Brunch
**Average price:** Inexpensive
**Area:** Ballsbridge
**Address:** 50 Serpentine Avenue Dublin 4
**Phone:** 353 1 6605049

#427
**Nyonya Malaysian Cuisine**
**Cuisines:** Malaysian
**Average price:** Modest
**Area:** South Inner City
**Address:** 76 Dame St Dublin 2
**Phone:** 353 1 6707200

#428
**Pig & Heifer**
**Cuisines:** Diner, Deli
**Average price:** Inexpensive
**Area:** Gardiner St
**Address:** 6 Guild Court Dublin 1
**Phone:** 353 1 8365542

#429
**The Hungry Mexican Restaurant**
**Cuisines:** Mexican, Bar
**Average price:** Modest
**Area:** Bolton St
**Address:** 57 Bolton St Dublin 1
**Phone:** 353 1 5480126

#430
**Manor Take Away Foods**
**Cuisines:** Fast Food
**Average price:** Inexpensive
**Area:** Stoneybatter
**Address:** 47 Manor St Dublin 7
**Phone:** 353 1 8387253

#431
**Lido Café**
**Cuisines:** Fast Food
**Average price:** Inexpensive
**Area:** Grand Canal Dock
**Address:** 135A Pearse St Dublin 2
**Phone:** 353 1 6707963

#432
**Casa Pasta**
**Cuisines:** Italian
**Average price:** Modest
**Area:** Marino, Clontarf
**Address:** 55 Clontarf Rd Dublin 3
**Phone:** 353 1 8331402

#433
**Il Sorriso**
**Cuisines:** Italian
**Average price:** Modest
**Area:** Malahide
**Address:** New St Dublin
**Phone:** 353 1 8452584

#434
**Pattaya Chinese & Thai**
**Cuisines:** Chinese, Thai
**Average price:** Modest
**Area:** Neilstown
**Address:** 9th Lock Rd Dublin 22
**Phone:** 353 1 4138870

#435
**Madina Asian Food Co.**
**Cuisines:** Indian
**Average price:** Modest
**Area:** North Inner City
**Address:** 17 Moore St Dublin 1
**Phone:** 353 1 8734011

#436
**La Dolce Vita**
**Cuisines:** Italian
**Average price:** Modest
**Area:** Temple Bar
**Address:** 5 Music Hall Dublin 2
**Phone:** 353 1 7079786

#437
**Brasserie 7**
**Cuisines:** Irish
**Average price:** Modest
**Area:** North Inner City
**Address:** The Capel Building Dublin 7
**Phone:** 353 1 4707770

#438
**Indie Dhaba**
**Cuisines:** Indian, Tapas
**Average price:** Modest
**Area:** South Inner City
**Address:** 21-26 S Anne St Dublin 2
**Phone:** 353 1 7079898

#439
**Shanai Restaurant**
**Cuisines:** Indian
**Average price:** Modest
**Area:** Cabinteely
**Address:** Bray Rd Dublin 18
**Phone:** 353 1 2070817

#440
**Tower Cafe**
**Cuisines:** Cafe
**Average price:** Inexpensive
**Area:** South Inner City
**Address:** 7 Dawson St Dublin 2
**Phone:** 353 67 13250

#441
**Milano**
**Cuisines:** Italian
**Average price:** Modest
**Area:** South Inner City
**Address:** 38 Dawson St Dublin 2
**Phone:** 353 1 6707744

#442
**KC Peaches Wine Cave**
**Cuisines:** Wine Bar, Cafe
**Average price:** Modest
**Area:** South Inner City
**Address:** 28-29 Nassau St Dublin 2
**Phone:** 353 1 6336872

#443
**Anar**
**Cuisines:** Persian/Iranian
**Average price:** Modest
**Area:** Terenure
**Address:** 101 Terennure Rd E Dublin 6
**Phone:** 353 1 4920050

#444
**Boteco Brazil**
**Cuisines:** Coffee & Tea, Brazilian
**Average price:** Modest
**Area:** North Inner City
**Address:** 6 Ormond Quay Upper Dublin 7
**Phone:** 353 1 8749778

#445
**Bach 16**
**Cuisines:** Mediterranean, Wine Bar
**Average price:** Modest
**Area:** North Inner City
**Address:** 16 Bachelor's Walk Dublin 1
**Phone:** 353 1 8720215

#446
**Gourmet Burger Kitchen**
**Cuisines:** Burgers
**Average price:** Modest
**Area:** South Inner City
**Address:** 14 S William St Dublin 2
**Phone:** 353 1 6790537

#447
**Martino's Trattoria**
**Cuisines:** Italian
**Average price:** Modest
**Area:** Rathgar
**Address:** 97 Ranelagh Rd Dublin 6
**Phone:** 353 1 4976455

#448
**Lunch!**
**Cuisines:** Cafe
**Average price:** Inexpensive
**Area:** South Inner City
**Address:** 4 Lombard St East Dublin 2
**Phone:** 353 1 4743080

#449
**Harry's On The Green**
**Cuisines:** Bar, American
**Average price:** Modest
**Area:** South Inner City
**Address:** 2 Kings St South Dublin 2
**Phone:** 353 1 4758504

#450
**Washerwomans Hill Café**
**Cuisines:** Irish
**Average price:** Expensive
**Area:** Glasnevin
**Address:** 60 Glasnevin Hill Dublin 9
**Phone:** 353 1 8379199

#451
**Gourmet Burger Kitchen**
**Cuisines:** American, Burgers
**Average price:** Modest
**Area:** Swords
**Address:** Pavilion Shopping Centre
**Phone:** 353 1 8902422

#452
**Lemongrass Citywest**
**Cuisines:** Thai, Asian Fusion
**Average price:** Expensive
**Area:** Rathcoole
**Address:** Citywest Golf Hotel Dublin
**Phone:** 353 1 4588207

#453
**Slattery**
**Cuisines:** Pub, Gastropub, Sports Bar
**Average price:** Modest
**Area:** North Inner City
**Address:** 129 Capel St Dublin 1
**Phone:** 353 1 8746844

#454
**Outhouse**
**Cuisines:** Cafe
**Average price:** Modest
**Area:** North Inner City
**Address:** 105 Capel St Dublin 1
**Phone:** 353 1 8734999

#455
**TGI Friday's**
**Cuisines:** American
**Average price:** Modest
**Area:** Blanchardstown
**Address:** Blanchardstown Ctr Dublin 15
**Phone:** 353 1 8225990

#456
**Mizzoni's Pizza & Pasta Co.**
**Cuisines:** Italian, Fish & Chips, Pizza
**Average price:** Inexpensive
**Area:** South Inner City
**Address:** 60 Georges St Dublin 2
**Phone:** 353 1 2020472

#457
**Marsellas Take-Away**
**Cuisines:** Fast Food
**Average price:** Inexpensive
**Area:** Churchtown
**Address:** 2 Beaumount Avenue Dublin 14
**Phone:** 353 1 2982675

#458
**KC Peaches**
**Cuisines:** Deli, Wine Bar, Food
**Average price:** Modest
**Area:** South Inner City
**Address:** 2829 Nassau St Dublin 2
**Phone:** 353 1 6336872

#459
**Pizza E Porchetta**
**Cuisines:** Italian
**Average price:** Expensive
**Area:** Grand Canal Dock
**Address:** The Malting Tower Dublin 2
**Phone:** 353 1 6624198

#460
**Fitzsimons Temple Bar**
**Cuisines:** Pub, Dance Club, Gastropub
**Average price:** Modest
**Area:** Temple Bar
**Address:** 21-22 Wellington Quay
Dublin 2
**Phone:** 353 1 6779315

#461
**Arc Cafe Bar**
**Cuisines:** Pub, Gastropub
**Average price:** Modest
**Area:** Palmerstown
**Address:** Liffey Valley SC Fonthill Rd
Dublin 22
**Phone:** 353 1 6207003

#462
**Namaste India**
**Cuisines:** Indian
**Average price:** Modest
**Area:** Smithfield
**Address:** 88 N King St Dublin 7
**Phone:** 353 1 8733013

#463
**Pho Ta**
**Cuisines:** Vietnamese
**Average price:** Modest
**Area:** Temple Bar
**Address:** 6 Cope St Dublin 2
**Phone:** 353 1 6718671

#464
**Eddie Rockets City Diner**
**Cuisines:** Irish
**Average price:** Modest
**Area:** Blanchardstown
**Address:** Blanchardstown Shopping
Centre Dublin 15
**Phone:** 353 1 8222876

#465
**Cracked Nut**
**Cuisines:** Sandwiches, Breakfast & Brunch
**Average price:** Modest
**Area:** Harcourt
**Address:** 71 Camden St Dublin 2
**Phone:** 353 1 5375942

#466
**Diep At Home**
**Cuisines:** Thai
**Average price:** Modest
**Area:** Drumcondra, Ballybough
**Address:** 18 Drumcondra Rd Dublin 9
**Phone:** 353 1 8601000

#467
**Kites**
**Cuisines:** Chinese
**Average price:** Expensive
**Area:** Ballsbridge
**Address:** 15/17 Ballsbridge Terrace Dublin 4
**Phone:** 353 1 6607415

#468
**Bakers**
**Cuisines:** Cafe
**Average price:** Modest
**Area:** Milltown
**Address:** 34 Donnybrook Rd Dublin
**Phone:** 353 1 2605787

#469
**Baxter&Greene**
**Cuisines:** Coffee & Tea
**Average price:** Inexpensive
**Area:** Harcourt
**Address:** Harcourt Rd Dublin 2
**Phone:** 353 1 4781016

#470
**Lee Kee Chinese Restaurant**
**Cuisines:** Chinese
**Average price:** Modest
**Area:** Rotunda
**Address:** 100 Parnell St Dublin 1
**Phone:** 353 1 8044517

#471
**Ho Ho**
**Cuisines:** Chinese, Fast Food
**Average price:** Modest
**Area:** Rathgar
**Address:** 13 Upper Rathmines Rd Dublin 6
**Phone:** 353 1 4912462

#472
**Borzas Takeaway**
**Cuisines:** Coffee & Tea, Fast Food
**Average price:** Inexpensive
**Area:** Irishtown
**Address:** 5 Sandymount Green Dublin 4
**Phone:** 353 1 2694130

#473
**Apache Pizza**
**Cuisines:** Pizza
**Average price:** Inexpensive
**Area:** Drumcondra
**Address:** 4 Drumcondra Rd Lower Dublin 9
**Phone:** 353 1 8600338

#474
**Camile Thai**
**Cuisines:** Thai
**Average price:** Modest
**Area:** South Circular Rd
**Address:** South Circular Rd Dublin 8
**Phone:** 353 1 4166111

#475
**Aldo's Diner**
**Cuisines:** Diner
**Average price:** Modest
**Area:** Cabinteely
**Address:** Old Bray Rd, Cornelscourt
Dublin 18
**Phone:** 353 1 2899226

#476
**Alladins Cafe Restaurant**
**Cuisines:** Mediterranean,
Middle Eastern
**Average price:** Expensive
**Area:** Baggot St
**Address:** 129 Upper Leeson St Dublin 4
**Phone:** 353 1 6689793

#477
**Michael Byrne Fine Foods**
**Cuisines:** Deli, Cheese Shop,
Fruits & Veggies
**Average price:** Modest
**Area:** Irishtown
**Address:** 95 Sandymount Rd Dublin 4
**Phone:** 353 1 6602827

#478
**Farrington's**
**Cuisines:** Pub, Gastropub
**Average price:** Modest
**Area:** Temple Bar
**Address:** 29 East Essex St Dublin 2
**Phone:** 353 1 6715135

#479
**PÓG**
**Cuisines:** Salad, Juice Bar, Ice Cream
**Average price:** Modest
**Area:** North Inner City
**Address:** 32 Bachelors Walk Dublin
**Phone:** 353 86 3767208

#480
**Khan's Balti House**
**Cuisines:** Indian
**Average price:** Modest
**Area:** Donnybrook
**Address:** 51 Donnybrook Rd Dublin 4
**Phone:** 353 1 2697674

#481
**Flanagan's Restaurant**
**Cuisines:** American
**Average price:** Modest
**Area:** North Inner City
**Address:** 61 O'Connell St Upper Dublin 1
**Phone:** 353 1 8731388

#482
**Tuzo Mexican Kitchen**
**Cuisines:** Mexican
**Average price:** Inexpensive
**Area:** South Inner City
**Address:** 51B Dawson St Dublin 2
**Phone:** 353 1 6798814

#483
**Real Gourmet Burger**
**Cuisines:** Burgers, American
**Average price:** Modest
**Area:** Dún Laoghaire
**Address:** The Pavilion Dublin
**Phone:** 353 1 2846568

#484
**Pasta Fresca**
**Cuisines:** Italian
**Average price:** Modest
**Area:** South Inner City
**Address:** 2-4 Chatham St Dublin 2
**Phone:** 353 1 6792402

#485
**The Swedish Food Co.**
**Cuisines:** Caterers, Fast Food, Sandwiches
**Average price:** Inexpensive
**Area:** IFSC
**Address:** 5b Mayor Square Dublin 1
**Phone:** 353 1 6739869

#486
**Harvey Nichols Cafe**
**Cuisines:** European, Irish
**Average price:** Modest
**Area:** Windy Arbour
**Address:** Dundrum Town Centre
Dublin 14
**Phone:** 353 1 2910488

#487
**Eddie Rockets**
**Cuisines:** Diner, Fast Food
**Average price:** Modest
**Area:** Parnell Square
**Address:** Parnell St Dublin 1
**Phone:** 353 1 8728076

#488
**Yum Thai**
**Cuisines:** Thai
**Average price:** Inexpensive
**Area:** South Inner City
**Address:** Duke St Dublin 2
**Phone:** 353 1 6708975

#489
**The Restaurant**
**At Brown Thomas**
**Cuisines:** Desserts, Coffee & Tea
**Average price:** Exclusive
**Area:** South Inner City
**Address:** 88-95 Grafton St Dublin 2
**Phone:** 353 1 6056666

#490
**Brams Cafe**
**Cuisines:** Coffee & Tea,
Breakfast & Brunch
**Average price:** Inexpensive
**Area:** Marino
**Address:** 4 St Aidan's Park Rd Dublin 3
**Phone:** 353 1 8335610

#491
**Buffalo19**
**Cuisines:** American, Chicken Wings
**Average price:** Modest
**Area:** Rathmines
**Address:** 109 Lower Rathmines Rd Dublin 6
**Phone:** 353 1 4926570

#492
**Turks Head**
**Cuisines:** Pub, Dance Club, Gastropub
**Average price:** Modest
**Area:** Temple Bar
**Address:** 27 Parliament St Dublin 2
**Phone:** 353 1 6799701

#493
**Blarney Inn**
**Cuisines:** Irish, Pub
**Average price:** Modest
**Area:** South Inner City
**Address:** 47- 49 Kildare St Dublin 2
**Phone:** 353 1 6794388

#494
**The Candy Shop**
**Cuisines:** Sandwiches, Desserts
**Average price:** Modest
**Area:** Rotunda
**Address:** 1 N Frederick St Dublin 1
**Phone:** 353 1 8744522

#495
**Cafe Moda**
**Cuisines:** Coffee & Tea, Sandwiches
**Average price:** Inexpensive
**Area:** Rathmines
**Address:** 192 Lower Rathmines Rd Dublin 6
**Phone:** 353 1 4978919

#496
**Caracas Coffee House**
**Cuisines:** Cafe
**Average price:** Modest
**Area:** Sandyford
**Address:** Unit 5 Leopardstown Retail
Park Dublin 18
**Phone:** 353 1 2938902

#497
**Ann's Bakery**
**Cuisines:** Bakery, Irish
**Average price:** Inexpensive
**Area:** North Inner City
**Address:** 41 Mary St Dublin 1
**Phone:** 353 1 8727759

#498
**Bachelor's Wok**
**Cuisines:** Asian Fusion
**Average price:** Modest
**Area:** North Inner City
**Address:** 22 Bachelors Walk Dublin 1
**Phone:** 353 1 8728536

#499
**Munchies**
**Cuisines:** Coffee & Tea
**Average price:** Modest
**Area:** East Wall
**Address:** Eastpoint Business Park Dublin 3
**Phone:** 353 1 8555871

#500
**Antica Venezia**
**Cuisines:** Irish
**Average price:** Modest
**Area:** Rathgar
**Address:** 97 Ashfield Rd Dublin 6
**Phone:** 353 1 4974112

# TOP 450
# ARTS & ENTERTAINMENT

Recommended by Locals & Trevelers
(From #1 to #450)

#1
**Kilmainham Gaol**
**Category:** Museum, Historical Building
**Area:** Island Bridge
**Address:** Inchicore Rd Dublin 8
**Phone:** 353 1 4535984

#2
**Marsh's Library**
**Category:** Library
**Area:** Clanbrassil St
**Address:** St. Patrick's Close Dublin 8
**Phone:** 353 1 4543511

#3
**National Museum of Ireland**
**Category:** Museum
**Area:** South Inner City
**Address:** Kildare St Dublin 2
**Phone:** 353 1 6777444

#4
**Old Jameson Distillery**
**Category:** Museum, Tours,
Beer, Wine, Spirits
**Area:** Smithfield
**Address:** Bow St Dublin 7
**Phone:** 353 1 8072355

#5
**Samuel Beckett Bridge**
**Category:** Landmark
**Area:** IFSC
**Address:** Sir Rogerson's Quay Dublin 1

#6
**Garden of Remembrance**
**Category:** Memorial Garden, Park
**Area:** Parnell Square
**Address:** Parnell Square Dublin 1

#7
**Science Gallery Dublin**
**Category:** Museum
**Area:** South Inner City
**Address:** Pearse St Dublin 2
**Phone:** 353 1 8964091

#8
**Famine Memorial**
**Category:** Statues, Local Flavor
**Area:** IFSC
**Address:** Custom House Quay Dublin 1

#9
**The Brazen Head**
**Category:** Pub, Irish, Music Venues
**Area:** Thomas St
**Address:** 20 Bridge St Lower Dublin 8
**Phone:** 353 1 6779549

#10
**Irish Film Institute**
**Category:** Cinema, Cafe
**Area:** Temple Bar
**Address:** 6 Eustace St Dublin 2
**Phone:** 353 1 6795744

#11
**Rathmines Library**
**Category:** Library
**Area:** Rathmines
**Address:** 157 Rathmines Rd Dublin 6
**Phone:** 353 1 4973539

#12
**Phil Lynott Statue**
**Category:** Statue, Local Flavor
**Area:** South Inner City
**Address:** Harry St Dublin 2

#13
**The Little Museum of Dublin**
**Category:** Museum
**Area:** South Inner City
**Address:** 15 Saint Stephen's Green, Dublin 2
**Phone:** 353 1 6611000

#14
**Blessington St. Basin**
**Category:** Landmark, Park
**Area:** Inns Quay
**Address:** Blessington St Dublin 7
**Phone:** 353 1 2225278

#15
**The Corkscrew Wine Merchants**
**Category:** Beer, Wine, Spirits, Winery
**Area:** South Inner City
**Address:** 4 Chatham St Dublin 2
**Phone:** 353 1 6745731

#16
**Guinness Storehouse**
**Category:** Brewerie, Museum
**Area:** James' St
**Address:** St James's Gate Dublin 8
**Phone:** 353 1 4084800

#17
**Molly Malone Statue**
**Category:** Statue
**Area:** South Inner City
**Address:** College Green Dublin 2
**Phone:** 353 1 6057700

#18
**James Joyce Statue**
**Category:** Statue
**Area:** North Inner City
**Address:** North Earl St Dublin 1

#19
**The Bernard Shaw**
**Category:** Bar, Music Venues
**Area:** Harcourt
**Address:** 11-12 S Richmond St Dublin 2

#20
**Dun Laoghaire East Pier**
**Category:** Pier, Landmark
**Area:** Dún Laoghaire
**Address:** Dun Laoghaire Dublin
**Phone:** 353 1 2053855

#21
**National Gallery of Ireland**
**Category:** Museum, Art Gallery
**Area:** South Inner City
**Address:** Merrion Square West Dublin 2
**Phone:** 353 1 6615133

#22
**The Porterhouse Temple Bar**
**Category:** Pub, Irish, Music Venues
**Area:** Temple Bar
**Address:** 16-18 Parliament St Dublin 2
**Phone:** 353 1 6798847

#23
**St. Stephen's Green Bandstand**
**Category:** Landmark, Park
**Area:** South Inner City
**Address:** St. Stephen's Green Dublin 2

#24
**The Mezz**
**Category:** Pub, Music Venues, Dive Bar
**Area:** Temple Bar
**Address:** 23/24 Eustace St Dublin 2
**Phone:** 353 1 6707655

#25
**Bruxelles**
**Category:** Pub, Music Venues
**Area:** South Inner City
**Address:** 7-8 Harry St Dublin 2
**Phone:** 353 1 6775362

#26
**Daniel O'Connell Monument**
**Category:** Monument, Landmark,
Historical Buildings
**Area:** North Inner City
**Address:** O'Connell St Dublin 1

#27
**Abbey Gallery**
**Category:**Museum
**Area:** North Inner City
**Address:** 20 Upper Abbey St Dublin 1
**Phone:** 353 1 8727500

#28
**National Museum
of Natural History**
**Category:** Museum
**Area:** South Inner City
**Address:** Merrion St Dublin 2
**Phone:** 353 67 77444

#29
**Dublin City Library & Archive**
**Category:** Library
**Area:** South Inner City
**Address:** 138-144 Pearse St Dublin 2
**Phone:** 353 1 6744800

#30
**Merchant's Arch Bar**
**Category:** Irish, Pub, Music Venues
**Area:** Temple Bar
**Address:** 48-49 Wellington quay
Dublin 2
**Phone:** 353 1 6074010

#31
**Patrick Kavanagh Statue**
**Category:** Statue
**Area:** Baggot St
**Address:** Wilton Ter Dublin 2

#33
**The Merry Ploughboy
Irish Music Pub**
**Category:** Music Venues, Pub
**Area:** Rockbrook
**Address:** Edmondstown Rd Dublin 16
**Phone:** 353 1 4931495

#32
**Casino Marino**
**Category:** Landmark, Historical Building
**Area:** Marino
**Address:** Cherrymount Crescent Dublin 3
**Phone:** 353 31 8331618

#34
**Dublin Writers Museum**
**Category:** Museum
**Area:** Parnell Square
**Address:** 18 North Parnell Square Dublin 1
**Phone:** 353 1 8722077

#35
**Meeting House Square**
**Category:** Urban Plaza
**Area:** South Inner City
**Address:** Temple Bar Dublin 2
**Phone:** 353 1 2806654

#36
**The International Bar**
**Category:** Pub, Music Venues,
Comedy Club
**Area:** South Inner City
**Address:** 23 Wicklow St Dublin 2
**Phone:** 353 1 6779250

#37
**Vicar St.**
**Category:** Performing Arts,
Music Venues
**Area:** The Liberties
**Address:** 59 Thomas St Dublin
**Phone:** 353 1 7755800

#38
**The O2**
**Category:** Amphitheatre, Music Venues
**Area:** East Wall
**Address:** North Wall Quay Dublin 1
**Phone:** 353 1 8198888

#39
**The Spire**
**Category:** Landmark, Historical Buildings
**Area:** North Inner City
**Address:** O'Connell St Dublin 1

#40
**Grafton St.**
**Category:** Shopping Street
**Area:** South Inner City
**Address:** 33 Grafton St Dublin 2
**Phone:** 353 1 6796984

#41
**The Ark**
**Category:** Performing Arts, Playground
**Area:** Temple Bar
**Address:** 11A Eustace St Dublin 2
**Phone:** 353 1 6707788

#42
**Cineworld Cinemas**
**Category:** Cinema
**Area:** Parnell Square
**Address:** Parnell St Dublin 1
**Phone:** 353 1 520880444

#43
**St. Kevin's Park**
**Category:** Landmark, Park
**Area:** South Inner City
**Address:** Camden Row Dublin 8
**Phone:** 353 1 6612369

#44
**National Library of Ireland**
**Category:** Library
**Area:** South Inner City
**Address:** Kildare St Dublin 2
**Phone:** 353 1 6030200

#45
**Taste of Dublin**
**Category:** Festival
**Area:** Crumlin
**Address:** Iveagh Garden Dublin 2
**Phone:** 353 1 4780088

#46
**Chester Beatty Library**
**Category:** Library
**Area:** South Inner City
**Address:** The Clock Tower Building Dublin 2
**Phone:** 353 1 4070750

#47
**Thomas House**
**Category:** Music Venues, Pub, Dive Bar
**Area:** Thomas St
**Address:** 86 Thomas St Dublin 8
**Phone:** 353 85 2039047

#48
**Le Bon Crubeen**
**Category:** French, Jazz & Blues
**Area:** North Inner City
**Address:** 81-82 Talbot St Dublin 1
**Phone:** 353 1 7040126

#49
**Poolbeg Lighthouse**
**Category:** Landmark, Historical Building
**Area:** Ringsend
**Address:** Pigeon House Rd Dublin 4

#50
**Bello Bar**
**Category:** Music Venues
**Area:** Harcourt
**Address:** Portobello Harbour Dublin 2
**Phone:** 353 86 3584435

#51
**Wellington Monument**
**Category:** Landmark, Monument
**Area:** Phoneix Park
**Address:** Phoenix Park Dublin 10

#52
**National Museum**
**Category:** Museum
**Area:** Smithfield
**Address:** Benburb St Dublin 7
**Phone:** 353 1 6777444

#53
**Oscar Wilde Statue**
**Category:** Statue, Landmark,
Historical Buildings
**Area:** South Inner City
**Address:** Merrion Square Park Dublin

#54
**Button Factory**
**Category:** Dance Club, Music Venues
**Area:** Temple Bar
**Address:** Curved St Dublin 2
**Phone:** 353 1 6709202

#55
**Joker's Chair**
**Category:** Memorial,Landmark
**Area:** South Inner City
**Address:** Merrion Square Park Dublin 2

#56
**Bord Gais Energy Theatre**
**Category:** Performing Arts
**Area:** Grand Canal Dock
**Address:** Grand Canal Dock Dublin 4
**Phone:** 353 1 6777999

#57
**The Four Courts Building**
**Category:** Landmark, Historical Building
**Area:** Thomas St
**Address:** 8 Merchants Quay Dublin 8
**Phone:** 353 1 8725555

#58
**Rory Gallagher Corner**
**Category:** Sculpture, Landmark,
Historical Buildings
**Area:** Temple Bar
**Address:** Meeting House Square
Dublin 2

#59
**The Book of Kells**
**Category:** Illuminated Manuscripts,
Historical Building, Museum
**Area:** South Inner City
**Address:** College St Dublin 2
**Phone:** 353 1 8962320

#60
**Hellfire Club**
**Category:** Landmark, Historical Building
**Area:** Arbour Hill
**Address:** 16 Montpelier Hill Dublin

#61
**The Twisted Pepper**
**Category:** Dance Club, Music Venues
**Area:** North Inner City
**Address:** 54 Middle Abbey St Dublin 1
**Phone:** 353 86 3252471

#62
**Slattery's**
**Category:** Pub, Music Venues
**Area:** Rathgar
**Address:** 217 Lower Rathmines Rd Dublin 6
**Phone:** 353 1 4972052

#63
**Charles Stewart Parnell Statue**
**Category:** Statue, Landmark
**Area:** Rotunda
**Address:** 5 Parnell Sq Dublin 1

#64
**Mythfest**
**Category:** Festival
**Area:** South Inner City
**Address:** Rose Garden Theatre Dublin 1
**Phone:** 353 83 1105488

#65
**Sin É**
**Category:** Pub, Music Venues, Dive Bar
**Area:** Four Courts
**Address:** 14-15 Upper Ormond
Quay Dublin 1
**Phone:** 353 1 5554037

#66
**Brendan Behan Statue**
**Category:** Statue
**Area:** Drumcondra
**Address:** Dorset St Dublin 7

#67
**Savoy**
**Category:** Cinema
**Area:** North Inner City
**Address:** 17 O'Connell St Upper Dublin 1
**Phone:** 353 1 520927004

#68
**Terenure Library**
**Category:** Library
**Area:** Terenure
**Address:** Templeogue Rd Dublin 6
**Phone:** 353 1 4907035

#69
**The Convention Centre Dublin**
**Category:** Performing Arts, Venues
**Address:** CCD Spencer Dock Dublin 1
**Phone:** 353 1 8560000

#70
**Irish Jewish Museum**
**Category:** Museum
**Area:** Portobello
**Address:** 3 Walworth Rd Dublin 8
**Phone:** 353 1 4531797

#71
**James Joyce Tower & Museum**
**Category:** Museum, Landmark,
Historical Building
**Area:** Glenageary
**Address:** Sandycove Point Dublin
**Phone:** 353 1 2809265

#72
**Jam Art Factory**
**Category:** Art Gallery, Museum,
Concept Shop
**Area:** Clanbrassil St
**Address:** 64/65 Patrick St Dublin 8
**Phone:** 353 1 6165671

#73
**Gate Theatre**
**Category:** Performing Arts
**Address:** 1 Cavendish Row Dublin 1
**Phone:** 353 1 8744045

#74
**The Forty Foot**
**Category:** Bathing Place,Landmark
**Area:** Glenageary
**Address:** N Sandycove Ave Dublin

#75
**Criminal Courts of Justice**
**Category:** Modern Building
**Area:** Phoenix Park
**Address:** Parkgate St Dublin 8

#76
**Dublinia**
**Category:** Museum
**Area:** Thomas St
**Address:** Winetavern St Dublin 8
**Phone:** 353 1 6794611

#77
**Hungry Tree**
**Category:** Landmark
**Address:** Henrietta St Dublin 1

#78
**Peadar Kearney's**
**Category:** Pub, Sports Bar,
Music Venues
**Area:** South Inner City
**Address:** 64 Dame St Dublin 2
**Phone:** 353 85 7267078

#79
**The Poolbeg Chimneys**
**Category:** Landmark
**Area:** Ringsend
**Address:** Ringsend Dublin 4

#80
**National Photographic Archive**
**Category:** Art Gallery
**Area:** Temple Bar
**Address:** Meeting House Square Dublin 2
**Phone:** 353 1 6030370

#81
**O'Connell Bridge**
**Category:** Landmark, Historical Buildings
**Address:** The River Liffey Dublin

#82
**JJ Smyth's**
**Category:** Pub, Jazz & Blues
**Area:** South Inner City
**Address:** 12 Aungier St Dublin 2
**Phone:** 353 1 4752565

#83
**Custom House**
Category: Landmark, Historical Building
Area: IFSC
Address: 1 Custom House Quay Dublin 1
Phone: 353 1 8882000

#84
**The Abbey Theatre**
Category: Performing Arts
Address: 26 Lower Abbey St Dublin 1
Phone: 353 1 8748741

#85
**Robert Emmet Statue**
Category: Statue, Landmark
Area: South Inner City
Address: St. Stephen's Green Dublin 2

#86
**The Workman's Club**
Category: Music Venues
Area: Temple Bar
Address: 10 Wellington Quay Dublin 2
Phone: 353 1 6706692

#87
**Swan Cinemas**
Category: Cinema
Area: Rathmines
Address: Lower Rathmines Rd Dublin 6
Phone: 353 1 520880007

#88
**CoisCéim Dance Theatre**
Category: Performing Arts,
Dance School
Area: North Inner City
Address: 14 Sackville Place Dublin 1
Phone: 353 1 8780558

#89
**Leinster House**
Category: Landmark, Historical Building
Area: South Inner City
Address: Kildare St Dublin 2
Phone: 353 1 6030200

#90
**Shelbourne Park Greyhound Stadium**
Category: Stadium
Area: Ballsbridge
Address: Shelbourne Park Dublin 4
Phone: 353 1 890269969

#91
**The Four Courts**
Category: Landmark, Historical Building
Address: Inns Quay Dublin

#92
**Royal Dublin Society**
Category: Stadium
Area: Ballsbridge
Address: Merrion Rd Dublin 4
Phone: 353 1 6680866

#93
**National Print Museum**
Category: Museum
Area: Baggot St
Address: Haddington Rd Dublin 4
Phone: 353 1 6603770

#94
**St Mary's Pro-Cathedral**
Category: Church, Historical Building
Area: North Inner City
Address: 83 Marlborough St Dublin 1
Phone: 353 1 8745441

#95
**Club Chonradh na Gaeilge**
Category: Pub, Lounge, Music Venues
Area: Harcourt
Address: 6 Sráid Fhearchair Dublin 2
Phone: 353 1 4751480

#96
**US Embassy Dublin**
Category: Landmark, Modern Building
Area: Ballsbridge
Address: 42 Elgin Rd Dublin 4
Phone: 353 1 6688777

#97
**National Leprechaun Museum**
Category: Museum
Area: North Inner City
Address: Jervis St Dublin 1
Phone: 353 1 8733899

#98
**National War Memorial Garden**
Category: Landmark, Garden
Area: Island Bridge
Address: Islandbridge Dublin 8

#99
**Dublin City Council**
Category: Historical Building
Area: Wood Quay
Address: Wood Quay Dublin 8
Phone: 353 1 6722222

#100
**Odeon Cinema**
**Category:** Cinema
**Area:** East Wall
**Address:** Point Village Dublin 1
**Phone:** 353 1 520880000

#101
**Central Library**
**Category:** Library
**Area:** North Inner City
**Address:** Henry St Dublin 1
**Phone:** 353 1 8734333

#102
**The Long Room**
**Category:** Museum, Local Flavor
**Area:** South Inner City
**Address:** Trinity College Dublin 2
**Phone:** 353 1 8961000

#103
**Georgian House Museum**
**Category:** Museum, Historical Building
**Area:** Baggot St
**Address:** 29 Lower Fitzwilliam St Dublin 2
**Phone:** 353 1 7026165

#104
**The Aviva Stadium**
**Category:** Stadium
**Area:** Beggars Bush
**Address:** 62 Lansdowne Rd Dublin 4
**Phone:** 353 1 2382300

#105
**Cúchulainn Statue**
**Category:** Statue, Local Flavor
**Area:** North Inner City
**Address:** O'Connelll St Dublin 1

#106
**Smock Alley Theatre**
**Category:** Performing Arts,
Venues, Event Space
**Area:** Temple Bar
**Address:** 6/7 Exchange St Lower Dublin 8
**Phone:** 353 1 6770014

#107
**Ilac Business Library**
**Category:** Library
**Area:** South Inner City
**Address:** Henry St Dublin 1
**Phone:** 353 1 0700996

#108
**The Globe**
**Category:** Pub, Jazz & Blues
**Area:** South Inner City
**Address:** 11 S Great George's St Dublin 2
**Phone:** 353 1 6711220

#109
**Croke Park Stadium**
**Category:** Stadium
**Area:** Ballybough
**Address:** Jones Rd Dublin

#110
**Museum Building**
**Category:** Museum, Historical Building
**Area:** South Inner City
**Address:** Trinity College Dublin Dublin 2
**Phone:** 353 1 8961000

#111
**Africa Calls Gallery**
**Category:** Museum
**Area:** Temple Bar
**Address:** 2 Temple Lane Dublin 2
**Phone:** 353 1 6715107

#112
**The Gaiety Theatre**
**Category:** Performing Arts
**Area:** South Inner City
**Address:** South King St Dublin 2
**Phone:** 353 1 6771717

#113
**Legends Bar**
**Category:** Music Venues, Pub
**Area:** South Inner City
**Address:** 16-18 Lord Edward St Dublin 2
**Phone:** 353 1 6708777

#114
**Three Fates**
**Category:** Fountain, Local Flavor
**Area:** South Inner City
**Address:** St Stephens Green Dublin

#115
**Andrews Lane Theatre**
**Category:** Dance Club, Bar,
Music Venues
**Area:** South Inner City
**Address:** 9 St Andrews Lane Dublin 2
**Phone:** 353 87 7378807

#116
**Defence Forces Memorial**
**Category:** Memorial, Landmark
**Area:** South Inner City
**Address:** Merrion Square Dublin 2

#117
**Irish Traditional Music Archive**
**Category:** Library
**Area:** South Inner City
**Address:** 63 Merrion Square Dublin 2
**Phone:** 353 1 6619699

#118
**Peacock Theatre**
**Category:** Performing Arts
**Area:** North Inner City
**Address:** Lower Abbey St Dublin 1
**Phone:** 353 1 8787222

#119
**Theatre Space @ The Mint**
**Category:** Performing Arts
**Area:** North Inner City
**Address:** 6 Henry Place Dublin 1
**Phone:** 353 1 8729977

#120
**O'Reilly Theatre**
**Category:** Performing Arts
**Area:** Rotunda
**Address:** Great Denmark St Dublin 1
**Phone:** 353 1 8586644

#121
**King's Inn Park**
**Category:** Park, Landmark
**Area:** Phibsboro
**Address:** Phibsborough Rd Dublin 7

#122
**Tivoli Theatre**
**Category:** Performing Arts
**Area:** The Liberties
**Address:** 135-138 Francis St Dublin 8
**Phone:** 353 1 4544472

#123
**Lansdowne Rd Stadium**
**Category:** Stadium
**Area:** Beggars Bush
**Address:** Lansdowne Rd Dublin 4
**Phone:** 353 1 2382300

#124
**Portobello Bridge**
**Category:** Landmark
**Area:** Harcourt
**Address:** South Richmond St Dublin 6

#125
**Royal City of Dublin Hospital**
**Category:** Historical Building, Hospital
**Area:** Baggot St
**Address:** Upper Baggot St Dublin 4

#126
**The Village**
**Category:** Bar, Dance Club,
Music Venues
**Area:** South Inner City
**Address:** 26 Wexford St Dublin 2
**Phone:** 353 1 4758555

#127
**Monster Truck Gallery
and Studios**
**Category:** Art Gallery
**Area:** The Liberties
**Address:** 73 Francis St Dublin 8

#128
**Pembroke Library**
**Category:** Library
**Area:** Ballsbridge
**Address:** Anglesea Rd Dublin 4
**Phone:** 353 1 6689575

#129
**Ballyfermot Library**
**Category:** Library
**Area:** Ballyfermot
**Address:** Ballyfermot Rd Dublin 10
**Phone:** 353 1 6269324

#130
**The Teachers Club**
**Category:** Music Venues,
Performing Arts
**Area:** Parnell Square
**Address:** 36 Parnell Sq W Dublin 1
**Phone:** 353 1 8726944

#131
**4 Dame Lane**
**Category:** Bar, Dance Club,
Music Venues
**Area:** South Inner City
**Address:** 4 Dame Lane Dublin 2
**Phone:** 353 1 6790291

#132
**Sean O'Casey Bridge**
**Category:** Landmark
**Area:** IFSC
**Address:** Liffey River Dublin

#133
**Grand Canal Square**
**Category:** Commercial & Cultural Center
**Area:** Grand Canal Dock
**Address:** Grand Canal Dock Dublin 2

#134
**Dublin Fringe Festival**
**Category:**Festival, Local Flavor
**Area:** Temple Bar
**Address:** 12 E Essex St Dublin 2
**Phone:** 353 1 6792320

#135
**Killiney Bay**
**Category:** Landmark
**Area:** Killiney
**Address:** Dalkey Dublin

#136
**Point Theatre**
**Category:** Performing Arts
**Area:** South Inner City
**Address:** north wall quay Dublin
**Phone:** 353 1 8844527

#137
**Ambassador Event Centre**
**Category:** Cinema, Venues
**Area:** Parnell Square
**Address:** Parnell Square Dublin 1
**Phone:** 353 1 6725883

#138
**Meeting Place Hags
with the Bags**
**Category:** Statues, Local Flavor
**Area:** North Inner City
**Address:** Liffey St Dublin 1

#139
**Leeson Lounge**
**Category:** Pub, Music Venues
**Area:** Baggot St
**Address:** 148 Leeson Upper St Dublin 4
**Phone:** 353 1 6603816

#140
**Berkeley Library**
**Category:** Library
**Area:** South Inner City
**Address:** 2 College Green Dublin 2
**Phone:** 353 1 8961000

#141
**Croke Park**
**Category:** Stadium
**Area:** Ballybough
**Address:** Croke Park Dublin 3
**Phone:** 353 1 8192300

#142
**Chester Beatty Roof Garden**
**Category:** Landmark, Botanical Garden
**Area:** South Inner City
**Address:** Chester Beatty Library
Dublin 2
**Phone:** 353 1 4070750

#143
**Croppies Acre**
**Category:** Memorial Park
**Area:** Collins Barracks
**Address:** Ellis Quay Dublin 7
**Phone:** 353 1 6717083

#144
**Project Arts Centre**
**Category:** Performing Arts, Art Gallery
**Area:** Temple Bar
**Address:** 39 East Essex St Dublin 2
**Phone:** 353 1 6712321

#145
**Screen Cinema**
**Category:** Cinema
**Area:** South Inner City
**Address:** 2 Townsend St Dublin 2

#146
**Dublin City Hall**
**Category:** Museum
**Area:** South Inner City
**Address:** Dame St Dublin
**Phone:** 353 1 2222204

#147
**Ha'penny Bridge**
**Category:** Landmark
**Area:** Temple Bar
**Address:** Wellington and Ormond Quay,
River Liffey Dublin 2

#148
**Jim Larkin Statue**
**Category:** Statue, Landmark,
Historical Buildings
**Area:** North Inner City
**Address:** O'Connell St Dublin 1

#149
**Mew Funpalace**
**Category:** Performing Arts
**Area:** South Inner City
**Address:** 4 Burgh Quay Dublin 2
**Phone:** 353 1 6714014

#150
**Taylor's Three Rock Restaurant**
**Category:** Cabaret, Irish, Music Venues
**Area:** Kilmashogue
**Address:** Grange Rd Dublin 16
**Phone:** 353 1 4942311

#151
**Bust of Constance Markievicz**
**Category:**Bronze Bust
**Area:** South Inner City
**Address:** St Stephen's Green Dublin 2

#152
**Gallery of Photography**
**Category:** Art Gallery
**Area:** Temple Bar
**Address:** Meeting House Square
Dublin 2
**Phone:** 353 1 6714654

#153
**Stillorgan Orchard**
**Category:** Pub, Gastropub,
Music Venues
**Area:** Stillorgan
**Address:** 1 The Hill Dublin
**Phone:** 353 1 2886793

#154
**Yeats House**
**Category:** Historical Building
**Area:** South Inner City
**Address:** 82 Merrion Square Dublin 2

#155
**The Academy**
**Category:** Music Venues, Dance Club
**Area:** North Inner City
**Address:** 57 Middle Abbey St Dublin 1
**Phone:** 353 1 8779999

#156
**National Wax Museum Plus**
**Category:** Museum
**Area:** Rotunda
**Address:** 4 Foster Place,
Temple Bar Dublin 2
**Phone:** 353 1 6718373

#157
**Ringsend Library**
**Category:** Library
**Area:** South Inner City
**Address:** Fitzwilliam St Dublin 4
**Phone:** 353 1 6680063

#158
**Grangegorman Military Cemetery**
**Category:** Military Cemetery
**Area:** Cabra
**Address:** Blackhorse Ave Dublin 7

#159
**James Joyce Cultural Centre**
**Category:** Museum
**Area:** Rotunda
**Address:** 35 N Great George's St
Dublin 1
**Phone:** 353 1 8788547

#160
**Custom House Visitor Centre**
**Category:**Emporium
**Area:** North Inner City
**Address:** 55/56 Upper O'Connell St
**Phone:** 353 1 8733900

#161
**Laya Healthcare City Spectacular**
**Category:** Festival
**Area:** South Inner City
**Address:** Merrion Square Dublin 2

#162
**Phibsboro Library**
**Category:** Library
**Address:** Blackquire Bridge Dublin 7
**Phone:** 353 1 8304341

#163
**Parnell Park**
**Category:** Stadium
**Area:** Beaumont
**Address:** Collins Avenue Dublin 5
**Phone:** 353 1 8312099

#164
**Patrick Kavanagh Seat**
**Category:** Statue, Local Flavor
**Address:** Grand Canal Dublin 4

#165
**Mansion House**
**Category:** Historical Buildings
**Address:** Dawson St Dublin 2
**Phone:** 353 1 6761845

#166
**Samuel Beckett Theatre**
**Category:** Performing Arts
**Area:** South Inner City
**Address:** Trinity College Dublin 2
**Phone:** 353 1 8962461

#167
**The Black Door**
**Category:** Jazz & Blues, Music Venues
**Area:** Harcourt
**Address:** 58 Harcourt St Dublin 2
**Phone:** 353 1 4764606

#168
**The Music Association of Ireland**
**Category:** Performing Arts
**Area:** South Inner City
**Address:** 69 South Great
Georges Street Dublin 2
**Phone:** 353 1 4785368

#169
**Russells**
**Category:** Pub, Music Venues
**Address:** 60 Ranelagh Rd Dublin 6
**Phone:** 353 1 4977120

#170
**Jameson Dublin
International Film Festival**
**Category:** Festival
**Area:** South Inner City
**Address:** Dublin
**Phone:** 353 1 6877974

#171
**Gallery Zozimus**
**Category:** Art Gallery
**Area:** The Liberties
**Address:** 56 Francis St Dublin 8
**Phone:** 353 1 4539057

#172
**Universal Promotions**
**Category:** Performing Arts
**Area:** South Inner City
**Address:** 8 William Street South Dublin 2
**Phone:** 353 1 6337212

#173
**Block T**
**Category:** Music Venues, Art Gallery
**Area:** Smithfield
**Address:** 1-0 Haymarket Dublin 7
**Phone:** 353 1 5351014

#174
**Marino Library**
**Category:** Library
**Area:** South Inner City
**Address:** Marino Mart Dublin
**Phone:** 353 1 8336297

#175
**The Lotts Café Bar**
**Category:** Gastropub, Pub, Jazz & Blues
**Area:** North Inner City
**Address:** 9 Lower Liffey St Dublin 1
**Phone:** 353 1 8727669

#176
**Powerscourt Theatre**
**Category:** Performing Arts
**Area:** South Inner City
**Address:** 2nd Floor Dublin 2
**Phone:** 353 1 6111060

#177
**Denzille Cinema**
**Category:** Cinema
**Area:** South Inner City
**Address:** 13 Denzille Lane Dublin 2
**Phone:** 353 1 8894910

#178
**Focus Theatre**
**Category:** Performing Arts
**Area:** South Inner City
**Address:** 12 Fade Street Dublin 2
**Phone:** 353 1 6712509

#179
**Coppa Cafe**
**Category:** Art Gallery, Coffee & Tea
**Area:** South Inner City
**Address:** 15 Ely Place Dublin 2
**Phone:** 353 1 6618411

#180
**Down To Earth Theatre**
**Category:** Performing Arts
**Area:** Gardiner Street
**Address:** 3 Beresford Place Dublin 1
**Phone:** 353 1 8551736

#181
**The Wine Buff**
**Category:** Winery, Beer, Wine, Spirits
**Area:** Rathgar
**Address:** 51 Cullenswood Rd Dublin 6
**Phone:** 353 1 4983552

#182
**Rathmines & Rathgar
Musical Society**
**Category:** Performing Arts
**Area:** Rathgar
**Address:** 67 Upper Rathmines Rd Dublin 6
**Phone:** 353 1 4971577

#183
**Mission Alive**
**Category:** Performing Arts
**Area:** Gardiner Street
**Address:** 3 Beresford Place Dublin 1
**Phone:** 353 1 8881355

#184
**Draíocht**
**Category:** Performing Arts, Art Gallery
**Area:** Blanchardstown
**Address:** Blanchardstown Town
Centre Dublin 15
**Phone:** 353 1 8852622

#185
**Civic Museum**
**Category:** Museum
**Area:** South Inner City
**Address:** 55 South William Street Dublin 2
**Phone:** 353 1 6794260

#186
**The Good Bits**
**Category:** Dance Club, Music Venues
**Area:** Gardiner St
**Address:** Store St Dublin 1
**Phone:** 353 86 8262303

#187
**Royal Hibernian Academy**
**Category:** Museum, Art Gallery
**Area:** South Inner City
**Address:** 15 Ely Place Dublin 2
**Phone:** 353 1 6612558

#188
**Art Store**
**Category:** Museum
**Area:** South Inner City
**Address:** 56 Sth William Street Dublin 2
**Phone:** 353 1 6727284

#189
**Hands & Turn Theatre**
**Category:** Performing Arts
**Area:** South Inner City
**Address:** 56 Sth William Street Dublin 2
**Phone:** 353 1 6797967

#190
**National Stadium**
**Category:** Stadium
**Area:** South Circular Rd
**Address:** S Circular Rd Dublin 8
**Phone:** 353 1 4533371

#191
**International Puppet Festival**
**Category:** Performing Arts
**Area:** Monkstown
**Address:** C/O lambert Puppet Theatre
**Phone:** 353 1 4429010

#192
**Representative Church
Body Library**
**Category:** Library
**Area:** Windy Arbour
**Address:** Braemor Park Dublin 14
**Phone:** 353 1 4923979

#193
**Dr. Quirkey's Good Time Emporium**
**Category:** Arcade
**Area:** North Inner City
**Address:** 55-56 Upper O'Connell St Dublin 1
**Phone:** 353 1 8733900

#194
**Paul Kane Gallery**
**Category:** Museum
**Area:** South Inner City
**Address:** 53 South William Street Dublin 2
**Phone:** 353 1 6703141

#195
**Sol Art Gallery**
**Category:** Art Gallery
**Area:** South Inner City
**Address:** 8 Dawson St Dublin 2
**Phone:** 353 1 6750972

#196
**New Theatre**
**Category:** Performing Arts
**Area:** Temple Bar
**Address:** 43 E Essex St Dublin 2
**Phone:** 353 1 6703361

#197
**Century City Arcade**
**Category:** Arcade
**Area:** Parnell Square
**Address:** Parnell St Dublin 1

#198
**Portfolio on Francis St.**
**Category:** Art Gallery
**Area:** The Liberties
**Address:** 67-68 Francis St Dublin 8
**Phone:** 353 1 4537124

#199
**Thomas Moore Statue**
**Category:** Landmark, Historical Buildings
**Area:** South Inner City
**Address:** College Green Dublin 2

#200
**Celt**
**Category:** Music Venues
**Area:** North Inner City
**Address:** 108 Lower Gardener Dublin 9

#201
**The Duke Gallery**
**Category:** Museum
**Area:** South Inner City
**Address:** 17 Duke Street Dublin 2
**Phone:** 353 1 6703294

#202
**The Douglas Hyde Gallery**
**Category:** Art Gallery
**Area:** South Inner City
**Address:** Trinity College Dublin 2
**Phone:** 353 1 8961116

#203
**Betelnut City Art Centre**
**Category:** Museum
**Area:** South Inner City
**Address:** City Quay Dublin 2
**Phone:** 353 1 6169040

#204
**The Pearse Centre**
**Category:** Performing Arts
**Area:** South Inner City
**Address:** 27 Pearse St Dublin 2

#205
**The Green Gallery**
**Category:** Art Gallery
**Area:** South Inner City
**Address:** St Stephens Green Center
**Phone:** 353 85 1988441

#206
**The Frederick Gallery**
**Category:** Museum
**Area:** South Inner City
**Address:** 24 South Frederick Street Dublin 1
**Phone:** 353 1 6707055

#207
**The Race Night Company**
**Category:** Performing Arts
**Area:** Bolton Street
**Address:** 46 Bolton Street Dublin 1
**Phone:** 353 1 8745255

#208
**Croke Park Premium Level**
**Category:** Stadium
**Area:** Ballybough
**Address:** Croke Park Dublin 3
**Phone:** 353 1 8192316

#209
**Red Line Entertainment**
**Category:** Performing Arts
**Area:** Temple Bar
**Address:** Merchants Arch Dublin 2
**Phone:** 353 86 8505423

#210
**Bookcube Gallery & Bookshop**
**Category:** Art Gallery, Books
**Area:** Rathmines
**Address:** 203 Lower Rathmines Rd Dublin 6
**Phone:** 353 1 4961064

#211
**Images**
**Category:** Art Gallery, Framing
**Address:** Dun Laoghaire Shopping
Centre Dublin
**Phone:** 353 1 2806542

#212
**National Concert Hall**
**Category:** Music Venues
**Area:** Harcourt
**Address:** Earlsfort Terrace Dublin 2

#213
**The Boom Boom Room**
**Category:** Music Venues
**Address:** 70 Parnell St Dublin 1
**Phone:** 353 1 8732687

#214
**The Ruby Sessions**
Category: Jazz & Blues, Music Venues
Address: 9 College St Dublin 1
Phone: 353 1 671061

#215
**St Anthonys Little Theatre**
Category: Performing Arts
Area: Thomas Street
Address: 8 Merchants Quay Dublin 7
Phone: 353 1 6774980 1

#216
**The GAA Museum**
Category: Museum
Area: North Inner City
Address: St Josephs Avenue Dublin 3
Phone: 353 1 8192323

#217
**Yeah**
Category: Performing Arts
Area: South Inner City
Address: 54 Dawson Street Dublin 2
Phone: 353 1 6778955

#218
**Debbie Paul Studio & Gallery**
Category: Art Gallery
Area: Temple Bar
Address: 1 Cows Lane Dublin 8
Phone: 353 1 6751814

#219
**Dublin Tenement Experience**
Category: Museum
Area: Bolton Street
Address: 14 Henrietta St Dublin 1
Phone: 353 1 8748030

#220
**The Garda Museum & Archives**
Category: Museum
Area: South Inner City
Address: The Records Tower, Dublin
Phone: 353 1 6669998

#221
**Brooks Private Cinema**
Category: Cinema
Area: South Inner City
Address: Drury St Dublin 2
Phone: 353 1 6704000

#222
**Graphic Studio**
Category: Museum
Area: Temple Bar
Address: Cope Street Dublin 2
Phone: 353 1 6798021

#223
**Patrick Donald
Photography Gallery**
Category: Art Gallery
Area: South Inner City
Address: 8/9 Royal Hiberian Way
Dublin 2
Phone: 353 1 6815225

#224
**Sporting Emporium**
Category: Casino, Sports Bar
Area: South Inner City
Address: Anne's Lane Dublin 2
Phone: 353 1 7030600

#225
**BPM Promotions**
Category: Performing Arts
Area: Clanbrassil Street
Address: Christchurch Dublin 8
Phone: 353 87 2257233

#226
**The Jackpot**
Category: Casino
Area: Harcourt
Address: 20 Montague St Dublin
Phone: 353 1 4785858

#227
**Heartbeat of Home**
Category: Local Flavor, Performing Arts
Area: Grand Canal Dock
Address: Grand Canal Square Dublin 2

#228
**Jon Jon Museum**
Category: Art Gallery
Area: Grand Canal Dock
Address: Asgard Rd Dublin
Phone: 353 89 2191933

#229
**Irish Burlesque School**
Category: Opera & Ballet, Dance School
Address: Foley St Dublin 1
Phone: 353 86 3712151

#230
**Movie Fest**
Category: Festival
Address: Parnell St Dublin 1

#231
**Noah's Ark Loft Artists Studios**
Category: Performing Arts
Area: Parnell Square
Address: 2 Granby Row Dublin 1
Phone: 353 1 8734209

#232
**Crypt Arts Centre Dublin Castle**
Category: Museum
Area: South Inner City
Address: Dame Street Dublin 2
Phone: 353 1 6713387

#233
**Yeats Exhibition**
Category: Local Flavor, Museum
Address: Kildare St Dublin 2

#234
**Fab Productions Limted**
Category: Performing Arts
Area: South Inner City
Address: Dame Street Dublin 2
Phone: 353 1 6793351

#235
**Robo Steel**
Category: Art Gallery
Address: Cow's Lane Designer
Studio Dublin 2
Phone: 353 87 2369085

#236
**Mitchells Wine Shop**
Category: Winery
Address: Grange Rd Dublin 16
Phone: 353 1 4933816

#237
**The West Organisation**
Category: Performing Arts
Area: South Inner City
Address: 1 Dame Street Dublin 2
Phone: 353 1 4756853

#238
**Race Night International**
Category: Performing Arts
Area: Parnell Square
Address: 3 Parnell Street Dublin 1
Phone: 353 1 8641212

#239
**Pearse Museum**
Category: Museum
Area: Rathfarnham
Address: Grange Rd Dublin 16
Phone: 353 1 4934208

#240
**The Irish Print Gallery**
Category: Art Gallery
Area: Blackrock
Address: Blackrock Market Dublin

#241
**The Civic Theatre**
Category: Performing Arts
Area: Tallaght
Address: The Square Dublin 24
Phone: 353 1 4627477

#242
**Central Catholic Library**
Category: Library
Area: South Inner City
Address: 74 Merrion Sq Dublin 2
Phone: 353 1 6761264

#243
**Seamus Ennis Cultural Centre**
Category: Music Venues
Area: Garristown
Address: The Naul Dublin 1
Phone: 353 1 8020898

#244
**Temple Bar Gallery & Studio**
Category: Art Gallery
Area: Temple Bar
Address: 5-9 Temple Bar Dublin 2
Phone: 353 86 6178026

#245
**Colossus Casino Club**
Category: Casino
Area: South Inner City
Address: 5-5a Montague St Dublin 2
Phone: 353 1 4785858

#246
**Centuary City**
Category: Performing Arts
Area: Parnell Square
Address: Parnell Centre Dublin 1
Phone: 353 1 8724692

#247
**Jorgenson Fine Art**
**Category:** Museum
**Area:** South Inner City
**Address:** 29 Molesworth Street Dublin 2
**Phone:** 353 1 6619758

#248
**The Hallward Gallery**
**Category:** Art Gallery
**Area:** South Inner City
**Address:** 65 Merrion Sq S Dublin 2
**Phone:** 353 1 6621482

#249
**Euro Entertainment**
**Category:** Performing Arts
**Area:** South Inner City
**Address:** 28 Molesworth Street Dublin 2
**Phone:** 353 1 6766718

#250
**Number Twenty Nine**
**Category:** Museum
**Area:** South Inner City
**Address:** 29 Fitzwilliam St Lower
Dublin 2
**Phone:** 353 1 7026165

#251
**Drumcondra Library**
**Category:** Library
**Area:** Drumcondra
**Address:** Millmount Avenue Dublin 9
**Phone:** 353 1 8377206

#252
**The Irish House Party**
**Category:** Music Venues, Irish
**Area:** The Liberties
**Address:** 19 Francis St Dublin 8
**Phone:** 353 1 6618410

#253
**Marino Library**
**Category:** Library
**Area:** Marino
**Address:** 14-20 Marino Mart Dublin 3
**Phone:** 353 1 8336297

#254
**Urban Retreat Gallery**
**Category:** Art Gallery
**Address:** Hanover Quay Dublin 2
**Phone:** 353 1 4785159

#255
**Ambassador Theatre**
**Category:** Performing Arts,
Music Venues, Museum
**Area:** North Inner City
**Address:** O'Connell St Dublin 1
**Phone:** 353 818 333773

#256
**Inchicore Library**
**Category:** Library
**Area:** Kilmainham
**Address:** 34 Emmet Rd Dublin 8
**Phone:** 353 1 4533793

#257
**Screen Cinema**
**Category:** Cinema
**Area:** South Inner City
**Address:** D'Olier St Dublin 2
**Phone:** 353 818 300301

#258
**Castle Music Exports**
**Category:** Performing Arts
**Area:** South Inner City
**Address:** Molesworth Street Dublin 2
**Phone:** 353 86 2452058

#259
**Hardwick St Womens
Resource Centre**
**Category:** Health Club, Beauty Centre
**Area:** Rotunda
**Address:** Apt 157 Hardwicke Street Dublin 1
**Phone:** 353 1 8734805

#260
**Dublin Fringe Theatre Festival**
**Category:** Performing Arts, Festival
**Area:** North Inner City
**Address:** Sackville Place Dublin

#261
**Caboom Creative Group**
**Category:** Performing Arts
**Area:** South Inner City
**Address:** 10 St Stephens Green Dublin 2
**Phone:** 353 86 8221518

#262
**Original Print Gallery**
**Category:** Museum
**Area:** Temple Bar
**Address:** 4 Temple Bar Dublin 2
**Phone:** 353 1 6773657

#263
**Paws in the Park**
Category: Festival
Area: North Inner City
Address: National Show Centre Dublin
Phone: 353 404 66855

#264
**Rubicon Gallery**
Category: Museum
Area: South Inner City
Address: 10 St Stephen's Green Dublin 2
Phone: 353 1 6708255

#265
**Theatre Upstairs**
Category: Performing Arts
Area: North Inner City
Address: 10 - 11 Eden Quay Dublin 1
Phone: 353 85 7727375

#266
**No Grants Gallery**
Category: Art Gallery
Area: Temple Bar
Address: 12 Essex St Dublin 2

#267
**Universal Music**
Category: Performing Arts
Area: South Inner City
Address: 9 Whitefriars Dublin 2
Phone: 353 86 2568633

#268
**Design Yard**
Category: Museum
Area: Temple Bar
Address: 12 East Essex St Dublin
Phone: 353 1 6778453

#269
**Donaghmede Library**
Category: Library
Address: Donaghmede Shopping Centre
Dublin 13
Phone: 353 1 8482833

#270
**Matchbox Theatre**
Category: Performing Arts
Area: South Inner City
Address: 13 S Great George's St
Dublin 2
Phone: 000 00 8079612

#271
**Tango Fiesta**
Category: Festival
Area: Parnell Square
Address: Parnell Sq Dublin 1
Phone: 353 86 3262416

#272
**Crumlin Leisure Centre**
Category: Leisure Centre
Area: South Inner City
Address: Crumlin Shopping cntr Dublin
Phone: 353 1 4544549

#273
**Passion Machine Theatre**
Category: Performing Arts
Area: Rotunda
Address: 30 Gardiner Place Dublin 1
Phone: 353 1 8788857

#274
**The National Gallery of Ireland**
Category: Art Gallery
Area: South Inner City
Address: Marlay Park House Dublin
Phone: 353 1 4051400

#275
**Ballymun Garda Station**
Category: Museum
Area: South Inner City
Address: Unit DEF 1 Floor,Town Centre
Phone: 353 1 6664400

#276
**Green On Red Gallery**
Category: Museum
Area: South Inner City
Address: 26 Lombard st E Dublin 2
Phone: 353 1 6713414

#277
**Vue**
Category: Cinema
Area: South Inner City
Address: Liffey Valley S.C Dublin

#278
**Hillsboro Fine Art Gallery**
Category: Art Gallery
Area: Parnell Square
Address: 49 Parnell Square West
Dublin 1
Phone: 353 1 8788242

#279
**Temple Theatre**
**Category:** Performing Arts
**Area:** Rotunda
**Address:** Temple Street Dublin 1
**Phone:** 353 1 8745008

#280
**Squirrel Music**
**Category:** Performing Arts
**Area:** South Inner City
**Address:** 5 Lombard Street Dublin 2
**Phone:** 353 1 6774603

#281
**The Market Studios**
**Category:** Art Gallery
**Area:** Four Courts
**Address:** St Mary's Lane Dublin
**Phone:** 353 1 8729155

#282
**County Library**
**Category:** Library
**Area:** Tallaght
**Address:** Library Square Dublin 24
**Phone:** 353 1 4620073

#283
**MadArt Gallery & Studio**
**Category:** Art Gallery
**Area:** Gardiner St
**Address:** 56 Lower Gardiner St Dublin 1
**Phone:** 353 1 8182039

#284
**Combridge Fine Art**
**Category:** Art Gallery
**Area:** South Inner City
**Address:** 17 Sth. William St Dublin 2
**Phone:** 353 1 6774652

#285
**Gormleys Fine Art**
**Category:** Museum
**Area:** South Inner City
**Address:** 24 S Frederick St Dublin 2
**Phone:** 353 1 6729031

#286
**Heraldic Artist**
**Category:** Local Flavor, Bookstore,
Art Gallery
**Area:** South Inner City
**Address:** 3 Nassau St Dublin 2
**Phone:** 353 1 6797020

#287
**Taxi Driver's Blessing**
**Category:** Landmark, Historical Buildings,
Local Flavor
**Address:** O'Connell St Dublin 1

#288
**George Salmon Statue**
**Category:** Landmark, Historical Buildings
**Address:** Front Square Dublin 2

#289
**The Rose Garden**
**Category:** Botanical Garden,
Venues, Event Space
**Area:** South Inner City
**Address:** New Square Dublin 2

#290
**Peoples Art**
**Category:** Art Gallery
**Area:** South Inner City
**Address:** St Stephens Green Dublin 2

#291
**Shauna's Video Store**
**Category:** Library
**Area:** South Inner City
**Address:** 5 Aungier Street Dublin 2
**Phone:** 353 1 4751611

#292
**The Oriel Gallery**
**Category:** Art Gallery
**Area:** South Inner City
**Address:** 17 Clare St Dublin 2
**Phone:** 353 1 6763410

#293
**The Amphitheatre**
**Category:** Amphitheatre
**Area:** Thomas St
**Address:** civic offices, Winetavern St

#294
**Artist On Merrion Sq.**
**Category:** Art Gallery
**Area:** South Inner City
**Address:** Merrion Sq N Dublin 2

#295
**Iveagh Gallery**
**Category:** Art Gallery
**Area:** The Liberties
**Address:** 38 Francis St Dublin 8
**Phone:** 353 87 7594478

#296
**Nag**
**Category:** Art Gallery
**Area:** The Liberties
**Address:** 59 Francis St Dublin 8
**Phone:** 353 87 6182100

#297
**Dublin Philharmonic Orchestra**
**Category:** Performing Arts
**Area:** South Inner City
**Address:** 22 St Stephens Green Dublin 2
**Phone:** 353 1 6627838

#298
**The Cross Gallery**
**Category:** Art Gallery
**Area:** The Liberties
**Address:** 59 Francis St Dublin 8
**Phone:** 353 1 4738978

#299
**Gaiety Theatre**
**Category:** Performing Arts
**Area:** Smithfield
**Address:** Sth King St Dublin 2
**Phone:** 353 1 6771717

#300
**Lemon Street Gallery**
**Category:** Museum
**Area:** South Inner City
**Address:** Lemon Street Dublin 2
**Phone:** 353 1 6710244

#301
**The Fitzwilliam Casino**
**& Card Club**
**Category:** Casino
**Area:** South Inner City
**Address:** Lower Fitzwilliam St Dublin 2
**Phone:** 353 1 6114677

#302
**PUCA Puppets**
**Category:** Performing Arts
**Area:** Inns Quay
**Address:** 36 Dominic Street Upper Dublin 11
**Phone:** 353 1 8304136

#303
**Aughrim St. Sports Hall**
**Category:** Recreation Center
**Area:** Stoneybatter
**Address:** Aughrim St Dublin 7
**Phone:** 353 1 8388085

#304
**Broadstone Studios**
**Category:** Performing Arts
**Area:** Inns Quay
**Address:** 40 Upper Dominick St. Dublin 7
**Phone:** 353 1 8301428

#305
**Louis Albrouze**
**Category:** Beer, Wine, Spirits, Winery
**Area:** Baggot St
**Address:** 127 Upper Leeson St Dublin 2
**Phone:** 353 1 6674455

#306
**MDM Entertainments**
**Category:** Performing Arts
**Area:** South Inner City
**Address:** 51 Pearse Street Dublin 2
**Phone:** 353 1 6727051

#307
**Blue Loft**
**Category:** Art Gallery
**Area:** Rathgar
**Address:** 121 Ranelagh Village Dublin 6
**Phone:** 353 1 4982666

#308
**Hidden Dublin Walking Tours**
**Category:** Museum
**Area:** Thomas Street
**Address:** Ushers Quay Dublin 8
**Phone:** 353 85 1023646

#309
**Whichcraft Gallery**
**Category:** Museum
**Area:** Smithfield
**Address:** Cows Lane Dublin 2
**Phone:** 353 1 4741011

#310
**Players Theatre**
**Category:** Performing Arts
**Address:** Samuel Beckett Centre Dublin 2
**Phone:** 353 1 8962242

#311
**Picketron Lotto Desk**
**Category:** Casino
**Address:** Jervis St Dublin 1
**Phone:** 353 1 8735263

#312
**1913 Lockout Pop Up Museum**
**Category:** Festival
**Address:** 383B North Circular Rd Dublin

#313
**St Marys Abbey**
**Category:** Museum, Church
**Address:** Meeting House Ln Dublin 1
**Phone:** 353 1 8721490

#314
**Gaiety Pantomime**
**Category:** Performing Arts, Local Flavor
**Address:** South King St Dublin 2

#315
**Theatre Works**
**Category:** Performing Arts
**Area:** South Inner City
**Address:** 112 St Stephens Green
Dublin 2
**Phone:** 353 1 4053944

#316
**The Sweetest Things Gift Shop**
**Category:** Flowers & Gifts
**Area:** Harold's Cross
**Address:** Sundrive Rd Dublin 12
**Phone:** 353 1 4063800

#317
**Ashtown Castle Visitor Centre**
**Category:** Museum
**Area:** Phoneix Park
**Address:** Phoenix Park Dublin
**Phone:** 353 1 6770095

#318
**Dundrum Library**
**Category:** Library
**Area:** Windy Arbour
**Address:** Lower Churchtown Rd Dublin 14
**Phone:** 353 1 2985000

#319
**Oddbins**
**Category:** Beer, Wine, Spirits, Winery
**Area:** Churchtown
**Address:** 125 Braemor Rd Dublin 14
**Phone:** 353 1 2963111

#320
**EnoWine**
**Category:** Winery
**Area:** Sandyford
**Address:** Burton House Dublin 1
**Phone:** 353 1 6360616

#321
**St Anthony's Theatre**
**Category:** Performing Arts
**Area:** Thomas Street
**Address:** Merchants Quay Dublin 2
**Phone:** 353 1 6706991

#322
**The Lyndsay Gallery**
**Category:** Art Gallery
**Area:** Dún Laoghaire
**Address:** 7a Monkstown Cres Dublin
**Phone:** 353 85 1551057

#323
**Kevin St. Library**
**Category:** Library
**Area:** South Inner City
**Address:** 18 Lower Kevin St Dublin 8
**Phone:** 353 1 4753794

#324
**Searsons Wine Merchants**
**Category:** Winery, Beer, Wine, Spirits
**Area:** Dún Laoghaire
**Address:** Monkstown Crescent Dublin
**Phone:** 353 1 2800405

#325
**Kidzone**
**Category:** Play & Party Centre
**Area:** Kinsealy
**Address:** Feltrim Rd Dublin
**Phone:** 353 1 8408749

#326
**The Song Room**
**Category:** Bar, Music Venues
**Area:** Lucan
**Address:** 11 S Great Georges St Dublin 2
**Phone:** 353 1 6711220

#327
**The Grand Social**
**Category:** Irish, Music Venues, Pub
**Area:** North Inner City
**Address:** 35 Lower Liffey St Dublin 1
**Phone:** 353 1 8740076

#328
**The Temple Bar Music Centre**
**Category:** Performing Arts
**Area:** Temple Bar
**Address:** Curved St Dublin 2
**Phone:** 353 1 6709202

#329
**Apollo Gallery**
**Category:** Art Gallery
**Area:** South Inner City
**Address:** 51c Dawson St Dublin 1
**Phone:** 353 1 6712609

#330
**Dublin Youth Theatre**
**Category:** Performing Arts
**Area:** Rotunda
**Address:** 23 Upper Gardiner Street Dublin 1
**Phone:** 353 1 8743687

#331
**Cultur**
**Category:** Performing Arts
**Area:** South Inner City
**Address:** 40 Kevin st Lower Dublin 8
**Phone:** 353 85 0202538

#332
**Leinster Gallery**
**Category:** Museum, Art Gallery
**Area:** South Inner City
**Address:** 28 South Frederick St Dublin 2
**Phone:** 353 1 6790834

#333
**Odeon Coolock**
**Category:** Cinema
**Area:** Marino, Clontarf
**Address:** 84 Malahide Rd Dublin 17
**Phone:** 353 1 8485133

#334
**No. 29 Lower Fitzwilliam St.**
**Category:** Museum
**Area:** Baggot St
**Address:** 29 Lower Fitzwilliam St. Dublin 2

#335
**Underground**
**Category:** Performing Arts
**Area:** Gardiner Street
**Address:** 76 Amiens Street Dublin 1
**Phone:** 353 1 8363781

#336
**The National Concert Hall**
**Category:** Music Venues
**Area:** Harcourt
**Address:** Earlsfort Ter Dublin 2
**Phone:** 353 1 4170077

#337
**Movievision**
**Category:** Library
**Area:** Smithfield
**Address:** 128 Church Street Dublin 7
**Phone:** 353 1 8735740

#338
**Shankill Library**
**Category:** Library
**Area:** Rathmichael
**Address:** 20 Library Rd Dublin 18
**Phone:** 353 1 2823081

#339
**Revenue Museum**
**Category:** Museum
**Area:** Rathfarnham
**Address:** Dublin Castle Dublin 2

#340
**The Library Project**
**Category:** Library
**Area:** Temple Bar
**Address:** 4 Temple Bar Dublin 2
**Phone:** 353 87 6856169

#341
**Graphic Studio Gallery**
**Category:** Art Gallery
**Area:** Temple Bar
**Address:** Cope St Dublin 2
**Phone:** 353 1 6798021

#342
**SFX City Theatre**
**Category:** Performing Arts
**Area:** Mountjoy
**Address:** 23 Sherrard Street Upper Dublin 1
**Phone:** 353 1 8554090

#343
**Ashford Gallery Rha**
**Category:** Museum
**Area:** South Inner City
**Address:** 15 Ely Place Dublin 2
**Phone:** 353 1 6617286

#344
**Ned Kelly's Sportsclub & Casino**
**Category:** Casino, Pool Hall
**Area:** North Inner City
**Address:** 43 Upper O' Connell St Dublin
**Phone:** 353 1 8732344

#345
**UGC Cinemas**
**Category:** Cinema
**Area:** South Inner City
**Address:** Parnell Centre Dublin
**Phone:** 353 1 8738450

#346
**Origan Art Gallery**
**Category:** Museum
**Area:** Harcourt
**Address:** 83 Harcourt Street Dublin 2
**Phone:** 353 1 4785159

#347
**Whyte's**
**Category:** Museum, Art Gallery
**Area:** South Inner City
**Address:** 38 Molesworth St Dublin 2
**Phone:** 353 1 6762888

#348
**Molesworth Gallery**
**Category:** Art Gallery
**Area:** South Inner City
**Address:** 16 Molesworth St Dublin 2
**Phone:** 353 1 6791548

#349
**Irish Craft Beer & Cider Festival**
**Category:** Festival
**Area:** IFSC
**Address:** CHQ Building Dublin

#350
**City Archives**
**Category:** Library
**Area:** South Inner City
**Address:** William Street Dublin 2
**Phone:** 353 1 6775877

#351
**National Museum
of Natural History**
**Category:** Museum
**Area:** South Inner City
**Address:** Merrion Square West Dublin
**Phone:** 353 1 6777444

#352
**Dublin Photographic Centre**
**Category:** Art Gallery
**Area:** Harcourt
**Address:** 10 Lower Camden St Dublin 2

#353
**Eblana Gallery**
**Category:** Art Gallery
**Area:** South Inner City
**Address:** 8 Lower Baggot St Dublin 2
**Phone:** 353 1 6788941

#354
**McNeils**
**Category:** Pub, Music Venues
**Area:** North Inner City
**Address:** 140 Capel St Dublin 1
**Phone:** 353 1 8747679

#355
**Cabra Library**
**Category:** Library
**Area:** Cabra
**Address:** Navan Rd Dublin

#356
**Mill Theatre**
**Category:** Performing Arts
**Area:** Dundrum
**Address:** Dundrum Town Centre Dublin 16
**Phone:** 353 1 2969340

#357
**Ladbrokes**
**Category:** Casino
**Area:** North Inner City
**Address:** 5 Lower Abbey St Dublin 1

#358
**Irish Life & Permanent**
**Category:** Museum
**Area:** South Inner City
**Address:** 53-56 St Stephens Green Dublin 2
**Phone:** 353 87 6391867

#359
**Buddha Bag Movie Lounge**
**Category:** Cinema
**Address:** Market Square Dublin 7
**Phone:** 353 1 8797601

#360
**Lisa Richards**
**Category:** Performing Arts
**Area:** South Inner City
**Address:** 15 Pembroke Street
Lower Dublin 2
**Phone:** 353 1 6624880

#361
**Edge**
**Category:** Casino
**Area:** Milltown
**Address:** 111 Rathmines Rd Dublin 6
**Phone:** 353 1 4971833

#362
**Finglas Library**
**Category:** Library
**Address:** Jamestown Rd Dublin 11
**Phone:** 353 1 8344906

#363
**Capital Videos**
**Category:** Library
**Area:** Parnell Square
**Address:** 21 North Frederick Street Dublin 2
**Phone:** 353 1 8730321

#364
**The Break-Away Project**
**Category:** Performing Arts
**Area:** South Inner City
**Address:** 15 Pembroke St Lower Dublin
**Phone:** 353 85 1496103

#365
**Blue Leaf Gallery**
**Category:** Museum, Art Gallery
**Area:** Marino
**Address:** 10 Marino Mart Dublin 3
**Phone:** 353 1 8335197

#366
**O'Leary's Amusements**
**Category:** Performing Arts
**Area:** The Liberties
**Address:** 41 Meath Street Dublin 8
**Phone:** 353 1 4542334

#367
**A1 Entertainment**
**Category:** Performing Arts
**Area:** Cork Street
**Address:** 103a New Cabra Road Dublin 7
**Phone:** 353 1 8380978

#368
**Tolka Rovers Sports Complex**
**Category:** Stadium
**Area:** Glasnevin
**Address:** Griffith Rd Dublin 11
**Phone:** 353 1 8379602

#369
**The Copper House Gallery**
**Category:** Art Gallery
**Area:** Harcourt
**Address:** Synge St Dublin

#370
**Children's Books Ireland**
**Category:** Performing Arts
**Area:** Harcourt
**Address:** 17 Lower Camden Street Dublin 2
**Phone:** 353 1 8725854

#371
**Irish Fine Art Plaster Work**
**Category:** Museum
**Area:** North Strand
**Address:** 24 Ossory Road Dublin 3
**Phone:** 353 1 8550150

#372
**Light House Cinema**
**Category:** Cinema
**Area:** Smithfield
**Address:** Market Square Smithfield, Dublin 7
**Phone:** 353 1 8728006

#373
**Kevin Sharkey Gallery**
**Category:** Art Gallery
**Area:** Temple Bar
**Address:** 5 Temple Lane South Dublin 2
**Phone:** 353 86 3760622

#374
**Steeple Sessions**
**Category:** Festival, Music Venues
**Area:** South Inner City
**Address:** 112 St. Stephen's Green
West Dublin 2
**Phone:** 353 1 6788470

#375
**Invasion Dublin**
**Category:** Festival
**Area:** Ballsbridge
**Address:** Merrion Rd Dublin 4
**Phone:** 353 85 8234994

#376
**City Centre Archives**
**Category:** Museum
**Area:** James' Street
**Address:** 130 James Street Dublin 8
**Phone:** 353 1 6792608

#377
**Hillsboro Fine Art**
**Category:** Museum
**Area:** Drumcondra
**Address:** 50 Botanic Avenue Dublin 9
**Phone:** 353 1 8367574

#378
**The Cobblestone**
**Category:** Pub, Music Venues
**Area:** Smithfield
**Address:** 77 North King St
Smithfield, Dublin 7
**Phone:** 353 1 8721799

#379
**The Irish Nautical Trust**
**Category:** Museum
**Area:** Grand Canal Dock
**Address:** South Docks Road Dublin 4
**Phone:** 353 1 6675275

#380
**Vintage Ireland**
**Category:** Festival
**Area:** Temple Bar
**Address:** P O Box 5057 Dublin D02
**Phone:** 353 87 2670607

#381
**Christies Fine Art Auctioneers**
**Category:** Museum
**Area:** Baggot Street
**Address:** 52 Waterloo Road Dublin 4
**Phone:** 353 85 0511344

#382
**Tzolkin St Graffiti Shop**
**Category:** Hobby Shop, Art Gallery
**Area:** Temple Bar
**Address:** 14 Wellington Quay Dublin
**Phone:** 353 87 0567785

#383
**Greenhills Archers**
**Category:** Archery Club
**Area:** South Inner City
**Address:** T.C.S. Sports Complex,
Castle Lawns Dublin 24

#384
**Presentation Models**
**Category:** Art Gallery
**Area:** South Inner City
**Address:** Crumlin Rd Dublin 12
**Phone:** 353 1 4539990

#385
**Lighthouse Cinema**
**Category:** Cinema
**Area:** Rialto
**Address:** 7 Reuben Plaza Dublin

#386
**The Olympia Theatre**
**Category:** Performing Arts
**Area:** South Inner City
**Address:** 72 Dames St Dublin
**Phone:** 353 1 4782153

#387
**Jack Pott's Bingo**
**Category:** Casino
**Area:** Cabra
**Address:** 60 Quarry Road Dublin 7
**Phone:** 353 1 8681748

#388
**Theatre@36**
**Category:** Performing Arts
**Area:** Parnell Square
**Address:** 36 Parnell Square, Dublin 1
**Phone:** 353 1 8726944

#389
**Skelton John**
**Category:** Museum
**Area:** Mount Brown
**Address:** 582 SCR Dublin 8
**Phone:** 353 1 4540375

#390
**Solomon Fine Art**
**Category:** Art Gallery
**Area:** South Inner City
**Address:** Balfe St Dublin 2
**Phone:** 353 86 8142380

#391
**Duke St. Gallery**
**Category:** Art Gallery
**Area:** South Inner City
**Address:** 17 Duke St Dublin
**Phone:** 353 1 6139005

#392
**The Lead White Gallery**
**Category:** Museum
**Area:** Ballsbridge
**Address:** Clyde lane Dublin 4
**Phone:** 353 1 6607500

#393
**The Betting Room**
**Category:** Leisure Center, Arcade
**Area:** South Inner City
**Address:** 78 Aungier St Dublin 2
**Phone:** 353 1 4783494

#394
**Cologne Art Investment**
**Category:** Museum
**Area:** Rathmines
**Address:** 1 Swanville Place Dublin 6
**Phone:** 353 1 4983255

#395
**The Barclay Club**
**Category:** Music Venues
**Area:** South Inner City
**Address:** Sth William St Dublin 2
**Phone:** 353 1 6770281

#396
**Kestrel Design & Art Studios**
**Category:** Museum
**Area:** Harold's Cross
**Address:** 230 Harolds Cross Rd Dublin 6w
**Phone:** 353 1 4962848

#397
**Kerlin Gallery**
**Category:** Museum
**Area:** South Inner City
**Address:** Anne's Lane Dublin 2
**Phone:** 353 1 6709093

#398
**Jack Pott's Bingo**
**Category:** Casino
**Area:** Crumlin
**Address:** Kildare Road Dublin 12
**Phone:** 353 1 4559659

#399
**Sharkey**
**Category:** Art Gallery
**Area:** South Inner City
**Address:** 35 Molesworth St Dublin
**Phone:** 353 89 2003679

#400
**UGC Cinemas Multiplex**
**Category:** Cinema
**Address:** Parnell Ctr Parnell St Dublin 1
**Phone:** 353 1 8728400

#401
**Talbot Gallery & Studios**
**Category:** Art Gallery
**Area:** IFSC
**Address:** 51 Talbot St Dublin 1
**Phone:** 353 1 8556599

#402
**Shortall-Stairs Art Advisers**
**Category:** Museum
**Address:** Dublin 6
**Phone:** 353 1 4901406

#403
**Taylor Gallery**
**Category:** Museum
**Area:** South Inner City
**Address:** 16 Kildare St Dublin 2
**Phone:** 353 1 6766053

#404
**Town & Country Fine Art Auctioneers**
**Category:** Museum
**Area:** North Inner City
**Address:** 4 Lower Ormond Quay
**Phone:** 353 1 8727401

#405
**Waldock Gallery**
**Category:** Museum
**Address:** Blackrock Shopping Centre B'rock Dublin 16
**Phone:** 353 1 2885657

#406
**Kevin Kavanagh Gallery**
**Category:** Museum
**Area:** South Inner City
**Address:** Chancery Lane Dublin 8
**Phone:** 353 1 4759514

#407
**Stone Gallery**
**Category:** Art Gallery
**Area:** South Inner City
**Address:** 70 Pearse St Dublin
**Phone:** 353 1 6711020

#408
**Wren Gallery**
**Category:** Museum
**Address:** 11 Martello Mews Dublin 4
**Phone:** 353 1 2698401

#409
**Jeanie Johnston**
**Famine Ship Museum**
**Category:** Museum
**Area:** IFSC
**Address:** Spencer Dock Dublin

#410
**Big's Bar**
**Category:** Bar, Music Venues
**Area:** Collins Barracks
**Address:** 30 Ellis Quay Dublin 7
**Phone:** 353 87 3601645

#411
**Inflight Audio**
**Category:** Arcade
**Area:** Belfield
**Address:** Block 7 Belfield Office
Park Dublin 4
**Phone:** 353 1 4125370

#412
**The Complex**
**Category:** Art Gallery
**Area:** Collins Barracks
**Address:** 72 Benburb St Dublin 7
**Phone:** 353 1 5446922

#413
**Peppercanister Gallery**
**Category:** Art Gallery
**Area:** Baggot St
**Address:** 3 Herbert St Dublin 2
**Phone:** 353 1 6611279

#414
**Harbour Bar**
**Category:** Pubs, Music Venues, Irish
**Address:** 1 Strand Road Bray
**Phone:** 353 1 2862274

#415
**Jorgensen Fine Art**
**Category:** Art Gallery
**Area:** Baggot St
**Address:** 75 Haddington Rd Dublin 4
**Phone:** 353 1 6673231

#416
**Rockfield Lounge**
**Category:** Pubs, Music Venues
**Address:** Dundrum Dundrum, Dublin 16
**Phone:** 353 1 2964650

#417
**Gate Theatre**
**Category:** Performing Arts
**Address:** 8 Parnell Square Dublin 1
**Phone:** 353 1 8744368

#418
**Waldock Gallery**
**Category:** Museum
**Area:** Navan Rd
**Address:** Priory Park Dublin
**Phone:** 353 1 2885657

#419
**Stewart's Sports Centre**
**Category:** Leisure Centre, Swimming
Classes
**Area:** Palmerstown
**Address:** Waterstown Avenue Dublin 20
**Phone:** 353 1 6269879

#420
**Loop Studios**
**Category:** Performing Arts
**Area:** North Inner City
**Address:** Space 28 North Lotts Dublin 1
**Phone:** 353 1 8720209

#421
**Elektra Studios**
**Category:** Performing Arts
**Area:** Temple Bar
**Address:** 8 Crow St Dublin 2
**Phone:** 353 1 6777134

#422
**White Lady Art**
**Category:** Art Gallery
**Area:** Temple Bar
**Address:** 14 Wellington Quay Dublin 2

#423
**White Lady**
**Category:** Art Gallery
**Area:** Temple Bar
**Address:** 14 Wellington Quay Dublin 2

#424
**Projects Arts Centre**
**Category:** Museum
**Area:** Temple Bar
**Address:** 39 East Essex St Dublin 2
**Phone:** 353 1 6796622

#425
**Comedy Cellar**
**Category:** Performing Arts
**Area:** South Inner City
**Address:** Wicklow St Dublin 2

#426
**5th Avenue Wedding Band**
**Category:** Performing Arts
**Area:** South Inner City
**Address:** Unit 12 Stephenstown
Ind Estate Dublin
**Phone:** 353 86 8133250

#427
**Château de Dublin**
**Category:** Museum
**Area:** South Inner City
**Address:** Dublin Castle Dublin 2

#428
**James Joyce's Dubliners**
**Category:** Performing Arts
**Area:** Rotunda
**Address:** 35 N Great Georges St Dublin
**Phone:** 353 1 8788547

#429
**James Joyce Center**
**Category:** Performing Arts
**Area:** Rotunda
**Address:** 35 N Great George's St Dublin
**Phone:** 353 1 8788547

#430
**National Museum**
**Category:** Museum
**Area:** South Inner City
**Address:** Collins Barracks Dublin
**Phone:** 44 1677 7444

#431
**Chancery Lane Theatre**
**Category:** Music Venues
**Area:** South Inner City
**Address:** Chancery Lane Dublin 2

#432
**Rubicon Gallery**
**Category:** Art Gallery
**Area:** South Inner City
**Address:** 10 Stephens Green Dublin 2
**Phone:** 353 1 6708053

#433
**Green on Red Gallery**
**Category:** Museum
**Area:** South Inner City
**Address:** 26-28 Lombard St East
Dublin 2
**Phone:** 353 1 6713414

#434
**Music Network**
**Category:** Performing Arts
**Area:** South Inner City
**Address:** The Coach House Dublin 2
**Phone:** 353 1 6719429

#435
**Tony Thursby**
**Category:** Performing Arts
**Area:** Portobello
**Address:** 29 Arnott St Dublin 8
**Phone:** 353 1 4540669

#436
**Focus Theatre**
**Category:** Performing Arts
**Area:** South Inner City
**Address:** 6 Pembroke Place Dublin 2
**Phone:** 353 1 6624677

#437
**Ticketmaster Ireland**
**Category:** Performing Arts
**Area:** Ballybough
**Address:** Croke Park Dublin 3
**Phone:** 353 1 8860996

#438
**Davis Gallery**
**Category:** Museum
**Area:** North Inner City
**Address:** 11 Capel Street Dublin 1
**Phone:** 353 1 8726969

#439
**Law Library**
**Category:** Library
**Address:** Church St Dublin 7
**Phone:** 353 1 8174593

#440
**The Sandford Gallery**
**Category:** Art Gallery
**Area:** Rathgar
**Address:** 100 Ranelagh Village Dublin 6
**Phone:** 353 1 4910320

#441
**Kick Start**
**Category:** Performing Arts
**Area:** Rathgar
**Address:** Rathmines Dublin
**Phone:** 353 85 1556601

#442
**Graphic Studio Dublin**
**Category:** Art Gallery
**Address:** 537 N Circular Rd Dublin 2
**Phone:** 353 1 8170942

#443
**Fitzwilliam Lawn Tennis Club**
**Category:** Stadium
**Address:** Appian Way Dublin 6
**Phone:** 353 1 6603988

#444
**Bombhouse Gallery**
**Category:** Art Gallery
**Address:** 20 - 25 Aldborough Ave
Dublin 1
**Phone:** 353 1 6767222

#445
**Von Gosseln**
**Category:** Museum
**Area:** South Inner City
**Address:** 11 Suffolk Street Dublin 2
**Phone:** 353 1 6714079

#446
**My First Canvas**
**Category:** Art Gallery
**Area:** Terenure
**Address:** 43 Terenure Rd North Dublin 6

#447
**Life Moulding**
**Category:** Art Gallery
**Address:** Ranelagh Village Dublin
**Phone:** 353 83 1309061

#448
**Garda Memorial Garden**
**Category:** Museum
**Area:** Clontarf
**Address:** Dublin Castle Dublin 1

#449
**W.A.G**
**Category:** Performing Arts
**Address:** Ringsend Dublin
**Phone:** 353 86 3374142

#450
**Ashtown Recording Studio**
**Category:** Performing Arts,
Video/Film Production
**Area:** Navan Rd
**Address:** Pelletstown House Dublin 7
**Phone:** 353 87 7981311

# TOP 500 NIGHTLIFE

The Most Recommended by Locals & Trevelers
(From #1 to #500)

#1
**The Stag's Head**
Category: Pub
Average price: Modest
Area: South Inner City
Address: 1 Dame Court Dublin 2
Phone: 353 1 6793687

#2
**Vintage Cocktail Club V.C.C**
Category: Cocktail Bar
Average price: Expensive
Area: Temple Bar
Address:15 Crown Alley Dublin 2
Phone: 353 1 6753547

#3
**The Long Hall**
Category: Pub
Average price: Modest
Area: South Inner City
Address:51 South Great
George's St Dublin 2
Phone: 353 1 4751590

#4
**Kehoe's**
Category: Pub
Average price: Modest
Area: South Inner City
Address:9 Anne St S Dublin 2
Phone: 353 1 6778312

#5
**L Mulligan Grocer**
Category: Pub, Irish
Average price: Modest
Area: Stoneybatter
Address:18 Stoneybatter Dublin 7
Phone: 353 1 6709889

#6
**The Porterhouse Temple Bar**
Category: Pub, Irish, Music Venues
Average price: Modest
Area: Temple Bar
Address:16-18 Parliament St Dublin 2
Phone: 353 1 6798847

#7
**The Brazen Head**
Category: Pub, Irish, Music Venues
Average price: Modest
Area: Thomas St
Address:20 Bridge St Lower Dublin 8
Phone: 353 1 6779549

#8
**Dice Bar**
Category: Pub, Dive Bar
Average price: Modest
Area: Smithfield
Address: 79 Queen St Dublin 7
Phone: 353 1 6333936

#9
**Mulligan's**
Category: Pub
Average price: Modest
Area: South Inner City
Address:8 Poolbeg St Dublin 2
Phone: 353 1 6775582

#10
**The Black Sheep**
Category: Pub
Average price: Modest
Area: Parnell Square
Address:61 Capel St Dublin 1
Phone: 353 1 8730013

#11
**Grogans Castle Lounge**
Category: Pub, Lounge
Average price: Modest
Area: South Inner City
Address:15 S William St Dublin 2
Phone: 353 1 6779320

#12
**Bruxelles**
Category: Pub, Music Venues
Average price: Modest
Area: South Inner City
Address:7-8 Harry St Dublin 2
Phone: 353 1 6775362

#13
**John Kavanagh**
Category: Pub
Average price: Inexpensive
Area: Glasnevin
Address:1 Prospect Square Dublin 9
Phone: 353 86 3745260

#14
**The Library Bar**
Category: Pub
Average price: Inexpensive
Area: South Inner City
Address:1 S Exchequer St Dublin 2
Phone: 353 1 6797302

#15
**Dublin Literary Pub Crawl**
**Category:** Tours, Pub
**Average price:** Modest
**Area:** South Inner City
**Address:**9 Duke St Dublin 2
**Phone:** 353 1 6705602

#16
**O'Donoghue's**
**Category:** Pub
**Average price:** Modest
**Area:** South Inner City
**Address:**15 Merrion Row Dublin 2
**Phone:** 353 1 6607194

#17
**O'Reilly's**
**Category:** Pub
**Average price:** Inexpensive
**Area:** South Inner City
**Address:**Tara St Station Dublin 2
**Phone:** 353 1 6716769

#18
**The Exchequer**
**Category:** Gastropub, Cocktail Bar
**Average price:** Modest
**Area:** South Inner City
**Address:**3-5 Exchequer St Dublin 2
**Phone:** 353 1 6706787

#19
**Mother**
**Category:** Dance Club
**Average price:** Modest
**Area:** Temple Bar
**Address:**Copper Alley Dublin 2
**Phone:** 353 1 6755025

#20
**P.Mac's**
**Category:** Coffee & Tea, Pub
**Average price:** Modest
**Area:** South Inner City
**Address:**Stephen St. Lower Dublin 2
**Phone:** 353 1 4053653

#21
**Slattery's**
**Category:** Pub, Music Venues
**Average price:** Expensive
**Area:** Rathgar
**Address:**217 Lower Rathmines Rd Dublin 6
**Phone:** 353 1 4972052

#22
**Hacienda Bar**
**Category:** Bar
**Average price:** Modest
**Area:** North Inner City
**Address:**15 Little Mary St Dublin 1
**Phone:** 353 1 8730535

#23
**Against the Grain**
**Category:** Pub
**Average price:** Modest
**Area:** South Inner City
**Address:**11 Wexford St Dublin 2
**Phone:** 353 1 4705100

#24
**Odessa**
**Category:** Breakfast & Brunch,
Brasserie, Wine Bar
**Average price:** Modest
**Area:** South Inner City
**Address:**13/14 Dame Court Dublin 2
**Phone:** 353 1 6703080

#25
**The Old Storehouse**
**Category:** Pub
**Average price:** Modest
**Area:** Temple Bar
**Address:**3 Crown Alley Dublin 2
**Phone:** 353 1 6074003

#26
**Whelans Live**
**Category:** Pub
**Average price:** Modest
**Area:** South Inner City
**Address:**25 Wexford St Dublin 2
**Phone:** 353 1 4780766

#27
**Toners Pub**
**Category:** Pub
**Average price:** Modest
**Area:** South Inner City
**Address:**139 Baggot St Lower Dublin 2
**Phone:** 353 1 6763090

#28
**Hole In The Wall**
**Category:** Lounge, Gastropub
**Average price:** Modest
**Area:** Navan Rd
**Address:**Blackhorse Avenue Dublin 7
**Phone:** 353 1 8389491

#29
**O'Connells**
**Category:** Pub
**Average price:** Inexpensive
**Area:** Harcourt
**Address:**29 South Richmond St Dublin 2
**Phone:** 353 1 4753704

#30
**The Temple Bar**
**Category:** Pub, Gastropub
**Average price:** Modest
**Area:** Temple Bar
**Address:**47/48 Temple Bar Dublin 2
**Phone:** 353 1 6725286

#31
**Merchant's Arch Bar**
**Category:** Irish, Pub, Music Venues
**Average price:** Modest
**Area:** Temple Bar
**Address:**48-49 Wellington quay Dublin 2
**Phone:** 353 1 6074010

#33
**The Gypsy Rose**
**Category:** Bar
**Average price:** Inexpensive
**Area:** Temple Bar
**Address:**5 Aston Quay Dublin 2
**Phone:** 353 86 3003490

#32
**Thomas House**
**Category:** Music Venues, Pub, Dive Bar
**Average price:** Modest
**Area:** Thomas St
**Address:**86 Thomas St Dublin 8
**Phone:** 353 85 2039047

#34
**Garage Bar**
**Category:** Dive Bar
**Average price:** Modest
**Area:** Temple Bar
**Address:**Essex St E Dublin 2
**Phone:** 353 1 6796543

#35
**The Merry Ploughboy**
**Irish Music Pub**
**Category:** Music Venues, Pub
**Average price:** Modest
**Area:** Rockbrook
**Address:**Edmondstown Rd Dublin 16
**Phone:** 353 1 4931495

#36
**Fibber Magees**
**Category:** Dance Club, Pub
**Average price:** Inexpensive
**Area:** Rotunda
**Address:**80 Parnell St Dublin 1
**Phone:** 353 1 8722575

#37
**The Sussex**
**Category:** Pub, Irish
**Average price:** Expensive
**Area:** Baggot St
**Address:**9 Sussex Terrace Dublin 4
**Phone:** 353 1 6762851

#38
**The Ginger Man**
**Category:** Pub
**Average price:** Modest
**Area:** South Inner City
**Address:**40 Fenian St Dublin 2
**Phone:** 353 1 6766388

#39
**The Front Lounge**
**Category:** Pub, Gay Bar
**Average price:** Modest
**Area:** Temple Bar
**Address:**33-34 Parliament St Dublin 2
**Phone:** 353 1 6704112

#40
**Palace Bar**
**Category:** Pub
**Average price:** Expensive
**Area:** Temple Bar
**Address:**21 Fleet St Dublin 2
**Phone:** 353 1 6717388

#41
**Button Factory**
**Category:** Dance Club, Music Venues
**Average price:** Modest
**Area:** Temple Bar
**Address:**Curved St Dublin 2
**Phone:** 353 1 6709202

#42
**The Duke**
**Category:** Pub
**Average price:** Modest
**Area:** South Inner City
**Address:**10 Duke St Dublin 2
**Phone:** 353 1 6799553

#43
**The Brew Dock**
**Category:** Pub
**Average price:** Modest
**Area:** IFSC
**Address:**1 Amiens St Dublin 1
**Phone:** 353 1 8881842

#44
**Cafe En Seine**
**Category:** Pub, Gastropub
**Average price:** Modest
**Area:** South Inner City
**Address:**40 Dawson St Dublin 2
**Phone:** 353 1 6774567

#45
**The Waterloo Bar & Grill**
**Category:** Pub, Gastropub, Cocktail Bar
**Average price:** Modest
**Area:** Baggot St
**Address:**36 Upper Baggot St Dublin 4
**Phone:** 353 1 6600650

#46
**Panti Bar**
**Category:** Gay Bar
**Average price:** Inexpensive
**Area:** North Inner City
**Address:**7-8 Capel St Dublin 1
**Phone:** 353 1 8740710

#47
**O'Neills Bar & Restaurant**
**Category:** Irish, Pub
**Average price:** Modest
**Area:** South Inner City
**Address:**2 Suffolk St Dublin 2
**Phone:** 353 1 6793656

#48
**The Twisted Pepper**
**Category:** Dance Club, Music Venues
**Average price:** Modest
**Area:** North Inner City
**Address:**54 Middle Abbey St Dublin 1
**Phone:** 353 86 3252471

#49
**The Dawson Lounge**
**Category:** Pub, Lounge
**Average price:** Modest
**Area:** South Inner City
**Address:**25 Dawson St Dublin 2
**Phone:** 353 1 6710311

#50
**The Bath**
**Category:** Pub
**Average price:** Modest
**Area:** Beggars Bush
**Address:**26 Bath Avenue Dublin 4
**Phone:** 353 1 6674687

#51
**37 Dawson St.**
**Category:** Bar
**Average price:** Modest
**Area:** South Inner City
**Address:**37 Dawson St Dublin 2
**Phone:** 353 1 9022908

#52
**Opium**
**Category:** Vietnamese, Cocktail Bar
**Average price:** Modest
**Area:** South Inner City
**Address:**26 Wexford St Dublin 2
**Phone:** 353 1 5267711

#53
**The Market Bar**
**Category:** Bar, Tapas Bar, European
**Average price:** Modest
**Area:** South Inner City
**Address:**14 Fade St Dublin 2
**Phone:** 353 1 6139094

#54
**The Cellar Bar**
**Category:** Bar
**Average price:** Modest
**Area:** South Inner City
**Address:**Upper Merrion St Dublin 2
**Phone:** 353 1 6030600

#55
**The Welcome Inn**
**Category:** Lounge
**Average price:** Inexpensive
**Area:** North Inner City
**Address:**93 Parnell St Dublin 1
**Phone:** 353 1 8743227

#56
**Doheny & Nesbitt**
**Category:** Pub
**Average price:** Modest
**Area:** Baggot St
**Address:**5 Baggot St Lower Dublin 2
**Phone:** 353 1 6762945

#57
**Le Bon Crubeen**
**Category:** French, Jazz & Blues
**Average price:** Expensive
**Area:** North Inner City
**Address:**81-82 Talbot St Dublin 1
**Phone:** 353 1 7040126

#58
**The Sugar Club**
**Category:** Dance Club
**Average price:** Modest
**Area:** Harcourt
**Address:**8 Lower Leeson St Dublin 2
**Phone:** 353 1 6787188

#59
**McNeils**
**Category:** Pub, Music Venues
**Average price:** Modest
**Area:** North Inner City
**Address:**140 Capel St Dublin 1
**Phone:** 353 1 8747679

#60
**The Yacht**
**Category:** Pub
**Average price:** Modest
**Area:** Clontarf
**Address:**73 Clontarf Rd Dublin 3
**Phone:** 353 1 8336364

#61
**The Auld Dubliner**
**Category:** Pub, Irish
**Average price:** Modest
**Area:** Temple Bar
**Address:**24-25 Temple Bar Dublin 2
**Phone:** 353 1 6770527

#62
**The Copper Bar**
**Category:** Bar, Steakhouse
**Average price:** Expensive
**Area:** Sandyford
**Address:**8 Blackthorne Rd Dublin 18
**Phone:** 353 1 2052033

#63
**Ukiyo Bar**
**Category:** Karaoke, Bar, Sushi Bar
**Average price:** Modest
**Area:** South Inner City
**Address:**7 Exchequer St Dublin 2
**Phone:** 353 1 6334071

#64
**Odeon**
**Category:** Dance Club, Cocktail Bar
**Average price:** Modest
**Area:** Harcourt
**Address:**57 Harcourt St Dublin 2
**Phone:** 353 1 4782088

#65
**The Bar With No Name**
**Category:** Pub, Wine Bar
**Average price:** Modest
**Area:** South Inner City
**Address:**3 Fade St Dublin 2
**Phone:** 353 1 6480010

#66
**Peadar Kearney's**
**Category:** Pub, Sports Bar,
Music Venues
**Average price:** Modest
**Area:** South Inner City
**Address:**64 Dame St Dublin 2
**Phone:** 353 85 7267078

#67
**The Marker Hotel**
**Category:** Bar, Hotel
**Average price:** Expensive
**Area:** Grand Canal Dock
**Address:**Grand Canal Square Dublin 2
**Phone:** 353 1 6875100

#68
**Scruffy Murphys**
**Category:** Pub
**Average price:** Inexpensive
**Area:** Baggot St
**Address:**1 Powers Ct Dublin 2
**Phone:** 353 1 6615006

#69
**The Confession Box**
**Category:** Pub
**Average price:** Inexpensive
**Area:** North Inner City
**Address:**88 Marlborough St Dublin 1
**Phone:** 353 1 8280028

#70
**Koh Restaurant
& Cocktail Lounge**
**Category:** Thai, Asian Fusion,
Cocktail Bar
**Average price:** Expensive
**Area:** North Inner City
**Address:**6/7 Jervis St Dublin 1
**Phone:** 353 1 8146777

#71
**The Church**
Category: Bar, Irish, Cafe
Average price: Modest
Area: North Inner City
Address:Mary St Dublin 1
Phone: 353 1 8280102

#72
**Ryan's Beggar's Bush**
Category: Pub
Average price: Inexpensive
Area: Beggars Bush
Address:115 Haddington Rd Dublin 4
Phone: 353 1 6682650

#73
**Yamamori Izakaya**
Category: Japanese, Bar
Average price: Modest
Area: South Inner City
Address:12-13 S Great George's St
Dublin 2
Phone: 353 1 6458001

#74
**Bowes Lounge**
Category: Pub
Average price: Inexpensive
Area: South Inner City
Address:31 Fleet St Dublin 2
Phone: 353 1 6714038

#75
**Bleecker St Cafe Bar**
Category: American, Cafe, Cocktail Bar
Average price: Modest
Area: Rotunda
Address:68 Dorset St Dublin 1
Phone: 353 1 8044459

#76
**The Ivy House**
Category: Pub, Sports Bar
Average price: Modest
Area: Drumcondra
Address:114 Drumcondra Rd
Upper Dublin 9
Phone: 353 1 8375385

#77
**Peruke & Periwig**
Category: Cocktail Bar
Average price: Expensive
Area: South Inner City
Address:31 Dawson St Dublin 2
Phone: 353 1 6727190

#78
**The Exchange Restaurant
& Cocktail Bar**
Category: American, Bar, Irish
Average price: Expensive
Area: South Inner City
Address:At College Green
Westmoreland St Dublin 2
Phone: 353 1 6451318

#79
**Mother Reilly's**
Category: Pub, European, Irish
Average price: Modest
Area: Rathgar
Address:30-32 Upper Rathmines Rd
Dublin 6
Phone: 353 1 4975486

#80
**Residence**
Category: European, Wine Bar
Average price: Exclusive
Area: South Inner City
Address:41 St. Stephen's Green Dublin 2
Phone: 353 1 6620000

#81
**McGowans of Phibsboro**
Category: Dance Club, Pub, European
Average price: Modest
Area: BRdstone
Address:18 Phibsboro Rd Dublin 7
Phone: 353 1 8306606

#82
**The Blue Light**
Category: Pub
Average price: Modest
Area: Stepaside
Address:Barnacullia Dublin 18
Phone: 353 1 2160487

#83
**Ri-Ra**
Category: Dance Club
Average price: Modest
Area: South Inner City
Address:Dame Court Dublin 2
Phone: 353 1 6711220

#84
**The Black Lion**
Category: Pub
Average price: Modest
Area: Inchicore
Address:207A Emmet Rd Dublin 8
Phone: 353 1 4534580

#85
**The Oak**
**Category:** Pub
**Average price:** Inexpensive
**Area:** South Inner City
**Address:**Dame St Dublin 2
**Phone:** 353 1 6717283

#86
**McGrattan's In The Lane**
**Category:** Pub, Irish
**Average price:** Modest
**Area:** South Inner City
**Address:**76-77 Fitzwilliam Lane Dublin 2
**Phone:** 353 1 6618808

#87
**Foggy Dew**
**Category:** Pub
**Average price:** Modest
**Area:** South Inner City
**Address:**1 Frownes St Upper Dublin 2
**Phone:** 353 1 6779328

#88
**W.J. Kavanagh's**
**Category:** Pub, Irish
**Average price:** Modest
**Area:** Rotunda
**Address:**4-5 Dorset St Dublin 1
**Phone:** 353 1 8730990

#89
**Rural Pub Tours**
**Category:** Tours, Pub
**Area:** South Inner City
**Address:**St. Andrew St Dublin 2
**Phone:** 353 87 9324036

#90
**Leeson Lounge**
**Category:** Pub, Music Venues
**Average price:** Modest
**Area:** Baggot St
**Address:**148 Leeson Upper St Dublin 4
**Phone:** 353 1 6603816

#91
**The Hairy Lemon**
**Category:** Pub, Gastropub
**Average price:** Modest
**Area:** South Inner City
**Address:**Stephen St Dublin 2
**Phone:** 353 1 6718949

#92
**The Boar's Head**
**Category:** Irish, Pub
**Average price:** Modest
**Area:** North Inner City
**Address:**149 Capel St Dublin 1
**Phone:** 353 1 8723107

#93
**The Old Stand**
**Category:** Pub
**Average price:** Inexpensive
**Area:** South Inner City
**Address:**37 Exchequer St Dublin 2
**Phone:** 353 1 6777220

#94
**The Dragon**
**Category:** Gay Bar
**Average price:** Modest
**Area:** South Inner City
**Address:**South Great George's St
Dublin 2
**Phone:** 353 1 4781590

#95
**Davy Byrnes**
**Category:** Gastropub
**Average price:** Modest
**Area:** South Inner City
**Address:**21 Duke St Dublin 2
**Phone:** 353 1 6775217

#96
**The Workman's Club**
**Category:** Music Venues
**Average price:** Modest
**Area:** Temple Bar
**Address:**10 Wellington Quay Dublin 2
**Phone:** 353 1 6706692

#97
**Copan**
**Category:** Bar, Dance Club
**Average price:** Modest
**Area:** Rathmines
**Address:**304 Lower Rathmines Rd
Dublin 6
**Phone:** 353 1 4060218

#98
**The Mezz**
**Category:** Pub, Music Venues, Dive Bar
**Average price:** Modest
**Area:** Temple Bar
**Address:**23/24 Eustace St Dublin 2
**Phone:** 353 1 6707655

#99
**Porterhouse North**
**Category:** Pub
**Average price:** Modest
**Area:** Drumcondra
**Address:**Cross Guns Bridge Dublin 9
**Phone:** 353 1 8309884

#100
**The Morgan Bar**
**Category:** Bar, Dance Club
**Average price:** Expensive
**Area:** Temple Bar
**Address:**10 Fleet St Dublin 2
**Phone:** 353 1 6437000

#101
**Olesya's Wine Bar**
**Category:** Wine Bar
**Average price:** Modest
**Area:** South Inner City
**Address:**18 Exchequer St Dublin 2
**Phone:** 353 1 6724087

#102
**Bison Bar & BBQ**
**Category:** Dive Bar, Barbeque
**Average price:** Modest
**Area:** Temple Bar
**Address:**11 Wellington Quay Dublin 2
**Phone:** 353 86 0563144

#103
**Stillorgan Orchard**
**Category:** Pub, Gastropub,
Music Venues
**Average price:** Modest
**Area:** Stillorgan
**Address:**1 The Hill Dublin
**Phone:** 353 1 2886793

#104
**Sin É**
**Category:** Pub, Music Venues, Dive Bar
**Average price:** Inexpensive
**Area:** Four Courts
**Address:**14-15 Upper Ormond Quay
**Phone:** 353 1 5554037

#105
**The Long Stone**
**Category:** Pub
**Average price:** Modest
**Area:** South Inner City
**Address:**10/11 Townsend St Dublin 2
**Phone:** 353 1 6718102

#106
**The Gin Palace**
**Category:** Cocktail Bar
**Average price:** Modest
**Area:** North Inner City
**Address:**42 Middle Abbey St Dublin 1
**Phone:** 353 1 8748881

#107
**The Pavillion**
**Category:** Bar, Gastropub
**Average price:** Inexpensive
**Area:** South Inner City
**Address:**Trinity College Dublin 2
**Phone:** 353 1 6081279

#108
**Sweeney's Bar**
**Category:** Pub
**Average price:** Modest
**Area:** South Inner City
**Address:**32 Dame St Dublin 2
**Phone:** 353 1 6350056

#109
**The Porterhouse Central**
**Category:** Pub, Gastropub
**Average price:** Modest
**Area:** South Inner City
**Address:**45-47 Nassau St Dublin 2
**Phone:** 353 1 6774180

#110
**Smyth's**
**Category:** Pub
**Average price:** Modest
**Area:** Rathgar
**Address:**75-77 Ranelagh Dublin 6
**Phone:** 353 1 4911075

#111
**TP Smiths**
**Category:** Pub, European, Gastropub
**Average price:** Modest
**Area:** North Inner City
**Address:**9-10 Jervis St Dublin 1
**Phone:** 353 1 8724031

#112
**The Swan Bar**
**Category:** Pub
**Average price:** Modest
**Area:** South Inner City
**Address:**16 Aungier St Dublin 2
**Phone:** 353 1 4752722

#113
**Dicey Reilly's**
**Category:** Bar, Gastropub, Dance Club
**Average price:** Inexpensive
**Area:** Harcourt
**Address:**21-25 Harcourt St Dublin 2
**Phone:** 353 1 4784841

#114
**Bagots Hutton Wine Emporium**
**Category:** Mediterranean, Wine Bar,
Cocktail Bar
**Average price:** Modest
**Area:** South Inner City
**Address:**28 S William St Dublin 2
**Phone:** 353 1 5343956

#115
**Peter's Pub**
**Category:** Pub
**Average price:** Modest
**Area:** South Inner City
**Address:**1 Johnstons Place Dublin 2
**Phone:** 353 1 6793347

#116
**O'Sheas Merchant**
**Category:** Bar
**Average price:** Modest
**Area:** Thomas St
**Address:**12 Bridge St Lower Dublin 8
**Phone:** 353 1 6793797

#117
**The Woolshed Baa & Grill**
**Category:** Sports Bar, Pub
**Average price:** Modest
**Area:** Parnell Square
**Address:**Parnell St Dublin 1
**Phone:** 353 1 8724325

#118
**The George**
**Category:** Gay Bar
**Average price:** Modest
**Area:** South Inner City
**Address:**89 S Great George's St Dublin 2
**Phone:** 353 1 4782983

#119
**Quays Bar**
**Category:** Pub
**Average price:** Modest
**Area:** Temple Bar
**Address:**Temple Bar Dublin 2
**Phone:** 353 1 6713922

#120
**Dame Tavern**
**Category:** Pub
**Average price:** Modest
**Area:** South Inner City
**Address:**18 Dame Court Dublin 2
**Phone:** 353 1 6793426

#121
**Howl At The Moon**
**Category:** Dance Club
**Average price:** Expensive
**Area:** Baggot St
**Address:**8 Lower Mount St Dublin 2
**Phone:** 353 1 6345460

#122
**The Schoolhouse
Bar & Restaurant**
**Category:** Gastropub, Pub, French
**Average price:** Modest
**Area:** Beggars Bush
**Address:**2-8 Northumberland Rd Dublin 4
**Phone:** 353 1 6675014

#123
**Café Bar H**
**Category:** Wine Bar, Mediterranean
**Average price:** Modest
**Area:** Grand Canal Dock
**Address:**Grand Canal Plaza Dublin 2
**Phone:** 353 1 8992216

#124
**KC Peaches**
**Category:** Deli, Wine Bar, Food
**Average price:** Modest
**Area:** South Inner City
**Address:**2829 Nassau St Dublin 2
**Phone:** 353 1 6336872

#125
**Acapulco Mexican Restaurant**
**Category:** Mexican, Tex-Mex, Bar
**Average price:** Modest
**Area:** South Inner City
**Address:**7 South Great Georges St
Dublin 2
**Phone:** 353 1 6771085

#126
**Brogan's**
**Category:** Pub
**Average price:** Modest
**Area:** South Inner City
**Address:**75 Dame St Dublin 2
**Phone:** 353 1 6799570

#127
**Neary's**
**Category:** Pub
**Average price:** Modest
**Area:** South Inner City
**Address:**1 Chatham St Dublin 2
**Phone:** 353 1 6778596

#128
**Fitzgerald's**
**Category:** Pub
**Average price:** Modest
**Area:** Temple Bar
**Address:**22 Astons Quay St Dublin 2
**Phone:** 353 1 6779289

#129
**The Liquor Room**
**Category:** Bar
**Average price:** Modest
**Area:** Temple Bar
**Address:**6-8 Wellington Quay Dublin 2
**Phone:** 353 87 3393688

#130
**Lost Society**
**Category:** Lounge, Cocktail Bar
**Average price:** Modest
**Area:** South Inner City
**Address:**South William St Dublin 2
**Phone:** 353 1 6111777

#131
**Kennedy Taverns**
**Category:** Pub
**Area:** South Inner City
**Address:**10 Georges Quay Dublin 2
**Phone:** 353 1 6770626

#132
**The Living Room**
**Category:** Pub, Sports Bar
**Average price:** Modest
**Area:** North Inner City
**Address:**Cathal Brugha St Dublin 1
**Phone:** 353 1 8727169

#133
**Ely Gastro Bar**
**Category:** Wine Bar
**Average price:** Modest
**Area:** Grand Canal Dock
**Address:**Grand Canal Square Dublin 2
**Phone:** 353 1 6339986

#134
**Capitol Lounge**
**Category:** Pub, Dance Club
**Average price:** Inexpensive
**Area:** South Inner City
**Address:**18/19 Lower Stephen's St
Dublin 2
**Phone:** 353 1 4757166

#135
**Barge Inn**
**Category:** Pub
**Average price:** Modest
**Area:** Harcourt
**Address:**42 Charlemount St Dublin 2
**Phone:** 353 1 4751869

#136
**The 51**
**Category:** Pub, Sports Bar
**Average price:** Modest
**Area:** Baggot St
**Address:**51 Haddington Rd Dublin 4
**Phone:** 353 1 6600150

#137
**57 The Headline**
**Category:** Pub
**Average price:** Modest
**Area:** South Circular Rd
**Address:**57, Lwr Clanbrassil St Dublin 8
**Phone:** 353 1 5320279

#138
**JW Sweetman Craft Brewery**
**Category:** Brewerie, Pub
**Average price:** Modest
**Area:** South Inner City
**Address:**1-2 Burgh Quay Dublin 2
**Phone:** 353 1 6705777

#139
**Dakota Bar**
**Category:** Cocktail Bar
**Average price:** Modest
**Area:** South Inner City
**Address:**9 S William St Dublin 2
**Phone:** 353 1 6727696

#140
**Hard Rock Cafe**
**Category:** Bar, American
**Average price:** Modest
**Area:** Temple Bar
**Address:**12 Fleet St Dublin 2
**Phone:** 353 1 6717777

#141
**BirchHall**
**Category:** Pub, Gastropub
**Average price:** Modest
**Area:** Rathgar
**Address:**129 Ranelagh Dublin 6
**Phone:** 353 1 4973985

#142
**Olympia Theatre**
**Category:** Performing Arts,
Music Venues
**Average price:** Modest
**Area:** South Inner City
**Address:**72 Dame St Dublin 2
**Phone:** 353 1 6793323

#143
**Doyles**
**Category:** Pub
**Average price:** Modest
**Area:** South Inner City
**Address:**9 College St Dublin 2
**Phone:** 353 1 6710616

#144
**Rody Bolands**
**Category:** Pub, Sports Bar
**Average price:** Modest
**Area:** Milltown
**Address:**12-14 Upper Rathmines Rd
Dublin 6
**Phone:** 353 1 4970328

#145
**Sackville Lounge**
**Category:** Pub
**Average price:** Inexpensive
**Area:** North Inner City
**Address:**16 Sackville Place Dublin 1
**Phone:** 353 1 8745222

#146
**The Harbourmaster**
**Category:** Pub, European
**Average price:** Modest
**Area:** IFSC
**Address:**Customs House Dock Dublin 1
**Phone:** 353 1 6701553

#147
**Pacinos**
**Category:** Italian, Dance Club
**Average price:** Modest
**Area:** South Inner City
**Address:**18 Suffolk St Dublin 2
**Phone:** 353 1 6775651

#148
**Farrington's**
**Category:** Pub, Gastropub
**Average price:** Modest
**Area:** Temple Bar
**Address:**29 East Essex St Dublin 2
**Phone:** 353 1 6715135

#149
**Toast Cafe Bar**
**Category:** Coffee & Tea, European,
Sports Bar
**Average price:** Modest
**Area:** Rathmines
**Address:**196 Rathmines Rd Lower
Dublin 6
**Phone:** 353 1 4126285

#150
**The Horseshoe Bar**
**Category:** Bar
**Average price:** Expensive
**Area:** South Inner City
**Address:**27 St Stephen's Green Dublin 2
**Phone:** 353 1 6634500

#151
**4 Dame Lane**
**Category:** Bar, Dance Club,
Music Venues
**Average price:** Modest
**Area:** South Inner City
**Address:**4 Dame Lane Dublin 2
**Phone:** 353 1 6790291

#152
**Ryan's Sandymount House**
**Category:** Pub
**Average price:** Modest
**Area:** Irishtown
**Address:**Sandymount Green Dublin 4
**Phone:** 353 1 2691612

#153
**The Mercantile Bar**
**Category:** Pub, Irish
**Average price:** Modest
**Area:** South Inner City
**Address:**28 Dame St Dublin 2
**Phone:** 353 1 6707100

#154
**La Caverna**
**Category:** Italian, Wine Bar, Diner,
Steakhouse
**Average price:** Expensive
**Area:** Temple Bar
**Address:**12 Fownes St Dublin 2
**Phone:** 353 1 6703110

#155
**Grand Central Cafe Bar**
**Category:** Gastropub, Pub, Steakhouse
**Average price:** Modest
**Area:** North Inner City
**Address:**10-11 Lower O'Connell St
Dublin 1
**Phone:** 353 1 8728658

#156
**Legends Bar**
**Category:** Music Venues, Pub
**Average price:** Modest
**Area:** South Inner City
**Address:**16-18 Lord Edward St Dublin 2
**Phone:** 353 1 6708777

#157
**Walters Café Bar & Restaurant**
**Category:** Gastropub, Pub, Cafe
**Average price:** Modest
**Area:** Dún Laoghaire
**Address:**68 Upper Georges St Dublin
**Phone:** 353 1 2807442

#158
**Foley's Bar**
**Category:** Pub, Irish
**Average price:** Modest
**Area:** South Inner City
**Address:**1 Merrion Row Dublin 2
**Phone:** 353 1 6610140

#159
**The Teachers Club**
**Category:** Music Venues,
Performing Arts
**Average price:** Inexpensive
**Area:** Parnell Square
**Address:**36 Parnell Sq W Dublin 1
**Phone:** 353 1 8726944

#160
**The International Bar**
**Category:** Pub, Music Venues,
Comedy Club
**Average price:** Modest
**Area:** South Inner City
**Address:**23 Wicklow St Dublin 2
**Phone:** 353 1 6779250

#161
**Tolka House**
**Category:** Pub, Irish
**Average price:** Modest
**Area:** Phone number
**Address:**Glasnevin Village Dublin 9
**Phone:** 353 1 8371082

#162
**Alfie's Restaurant**
**Category:** European, Bar
**Average price:** Modest
**Area:** South Inner City
**Address:**10 S William St Dublin 2
**Phone:** 353 1 6718767

#163
**McSorley's Pub**
**Category:** Pub, Venues, Event Space
**Average price:** Modest
**Area:** Rathgar
**Address:**3-5 Sandford Rd Dublin 6
**Phone:** 353 1 4979775

#164
**Houricans**
**Category:** Pub
**Average price:** Modest
**Area:** Phone number
**Address:**7 Lower Leeson St Dublin 2
**Phone:** 353 1 6789030

#165
**Bakers Bar & Restaurant**
**Category:** Pub, Sports Bar,
Coffee & Tea
**Average price:** Inexpensive
**Area:** The Liberties
**Address:**47-48 Thomas St Dublin 8
**Phone:** 353 1 4736789

#166
**House**
**Category:** Bar, Mediterranean
**Average price:** Expensive
**Area:** Harcourt
**Address:**27 Lower Leeson St Dublin 2
**Phone:** 353 1 9059090

#167
**Dylan Bar**
**Category:** Wine Bar, Champagne Bar
**Average price:** Expensive
**Area:** Baggot St
**Address:**Eastmoreland Place Dublin 4
**Phone:** 353 1 6603000

#168
**Sheehans**
**Category:** Pub
**Average price:** Modest
**Area:** South Inner City
**Address:**17 Chatham St Dublin 2
**Phone:** 353 1 6771914

#169
**Ely Bar & Brasserie**
**Category:** Brasserie, Wine Bar
**Average price:** Expensive
**Area:** IFSC
**Address:**Georges Dock, IFSC Dublin 1
**Phone:** 353 1 6720010

#170
**Beerhouse**
**Category:** Pub, Brewerie, Venues,
Event Space
**Average price:** Modest
**Area:** Bolton St
**Address:**199 King St North Dublin 1
**Phone:** 353 1 8047023

#171
**Thomas Read**
**Category:** Pub, Dance Club
**Average price:** Modest
**Area:** Temple Bar
**Address:**Parliament St Dublin 2
**Phone:** 353 1 6717283

#172
**Big Tree**
**Category:** Pub
**Average price:** Modest
**Area:** Ballybough
**Address:**39 Lower Dorset St Dublin 1
**Phone:** 353 1 8553403

#173
**Arthurs Pub**
**Category:** Pub
**Average price:** Modest
**Area:** James' St
**Address:**28 Thomas St Dublin 8
**Phone:** 353 1 4020914

#174
**Isabels**
**Category:** Wine Bar, Irish
**Area:** Baggot St
**Address:**112 Lower Baggot St Dublin 2
**Phone:** 353 1 6619000

#175
**Molloys Pub**
**Category:** Pub
**Average price:** Inexpensive
**Area:** Gardiner St
**Address:**59 Talbot St Dublin 1
**Phone:** 353 1 8550017

#176
**Kiely's Of Donnybrook**
**Category:** Sports Bar, Pub
**Average price:** Modest
**Area:** Ballsbridge
**Address:**22-24 Donnybrook Rd Dublin 4
**Phone:** 353 1 2830209

#177
**Bad Bobs**
**Category:** Cocktail Bar
**Average price:** Modest
**Area:** Temple Bar
**Address:**34-35 E Essex St Dublin 2
**Phone:** 353 1 6778860

#178
**The Bailey**
**Category:** Pub, Gastropub
**Average price:** Modest
**Area:** South Inner City
**Address:**Duke St Dublin 2
**Phone:** 353 1 6704939

#179
**Copper Face Jacks**
**Category:** Dance Club, Bar
**Average price:** Modest
**Area:** Harcourt
**Address:**29 Harcourt St Dublin 2
**Phone:** 353 1 4758777

#180
**Kavanaghs**
**Category:** Pub
**Area:** Castleknock
**Address:**Laurel Lodge Rd Dublin
**Phone:** 353 1 8205916

#181
**Bankers**
**Category:** Pub
**Average price:** Modest
**Area:** South Inner City
**Address:**16 Trinity St Dublin 2
**Phone:** 353 1 6793697

#182
**Anna Livia Executive Lounge**
**Category:** Bar
**Average price:** Modest
**Area:** Santry
**Address:**Dublin Airport Dublin 2
**Phone:** 353 1 8144501

#183
**Halfway House**
**Category:** Pub
**Average price:** Modest
**Area:** Navan Rd
**Address:**Navan Rd Dublin 7
**Phone:** 353 1 8383218

#184
**Andrews Lane Theatre**
**Category:** Dance Club, Bar,
Music Venues
**Average price:** Inexpensive
**Area:** South Inner City
**Address:**9 St Andrews Lane Dublin 2
**Phone:** 353 87 7378807

#185
**The Oval Bar**
**Category:** Pub
**Average price:** Modest
**Area:** North Inner City
**Address:**78 Middle Abbey St Dublin 1
**Phone:** 353 1 8721259

#186
**Dtwo**
**Category:** Dance Club, Sports Bar, Pub
**Average price:** Modest
**Area:** Harcourt
**Address:**60 Harcourt St Dublin 2
**Phone:** 353 1 4764603

#187
**The Gasworks Bar**
**Category:** Pub, Gastropub
**Average price:** Modest
**Area:** Grand Canal Dock
**Address:**Grand Canal St Dublin 4
**Phone:** 353 1 6461000

#188
**Twelfth Lock Bar**
**Category:** Sports Bar
**Average price:** Modest
**Area:** Blanchardstown
**Address:**Castleknock Marina, The Royal
Canal Dublin 15
**Phone:** 353 1 8607400

#189
**Pygmalion**
**Category:** Dance Club, Hookah Bar,
Cocktail Bar
**Average price:** Modest
**Area:** South Inner City
**Address:**59 South William St Dublin 2
**Phone:** 353 1 6334479

#190
**La Cave Winebar and Restaurant**
**Category:** Steakhouse, Wine Bar
**Average price:** Expensive
**Area:** South Inner City
**Address:**28 South Anne St Dublin 2
**Phone:** 353 1 6794409

#191
**The Gables/McCabes Wines**
**Category:** Bar, Mediterranean
**Average price:** Expensive
**Area:** Foxrock
**Address:**Torquay Rd Dublin 18
**Phone:** 353 1 2892174

#192
**Quinn's Public House**
**Category:** Pub
**Average price:** Modest
**Area:** Drumcondra
**Address:**42 Lower Drumcondra Rd
Dublin 9
**Phone:** 353 1 5378453

#193
**M O'Briens**
**Category:** Pub
**Average price:** Modest
**Area:** Phone number
**Address:**Sussex Ter Dublin 4
**Phone:** 353 1 6762851

#194
**Eden Bar and Grill**
**Category:** Wine Bar, Barbeque
**Average price:** Expensive
**Area:** South Inner City
**Address:**7 South William St Dublin 2
**Phone:** 353 1 6706887

#195
**MV Cill Airne**
**Category:** Pub
**Average price:** Modest
**Area:** East Wall
**Address:**North Wall Quay Dublin 1
**Phone:** 353 1 8178760

#196
**The Academy**
**Category:** Music Venues, Dance Club
**Average price:** Modest
**Area:** North Inner City
**Address:**57 Middle Abbey St Dublin 1
**Phone:** 353 1 8779999

#197
**Cassidy's**
**Category:** Pub
**Average price:** Modest
**Area:** Harcourt
**Address:**42 Lower Camden St Dublin 2
**Phone:** 353 1 4751429

#198
**Wallace's Taverna**
**Category:** Italian, Wine Bar
**Average price:** Modest
**Area:** North Inner City
**Address:**24 Lower Ormond Quay Dublin 1
**Phone:** 353 1 8730040

#199
**Bang Restaurant**
**Category:** Irish, European, Wine Bar
**Average price:** Expensive
**Area:** South Inner City
**Address:**11 Merrion Row Dublin 2
**Phone:** 353 1 4004229

#200
**Merrion Inn**
**Category:** Pub, Gastropub
**Average price:** Modest
**Area:** Merrion
**Address:**188 Merrion Rd Dublin 4
**Phone:** 353 1 2693816

#201
**The Lombard**
**Category:** Pub
**Average price:** Modest
**Area:** South Inner City
**Address:**1 Lombard St Dublin 2
**Phone:** 353 1 6085000

#202
**The Czech Inn**
**Category:** Gastropub, Pub
**Average price:** Modest
**Area:** Temple Bar
**Address:**Essex Gate Dublin 2
**Phone:** 353 1 6711535

#203
**No. 27 Bar & Lounge**
**Category:** Champagne Bar,
Pub, Wine Bar
**Average price:** Expensive
**Area:** South Inner City
**Address:**27 St Stephen's Green Dublin 2
**Phone:** 353 1 6634500

#204
**Slattery**
**Category:** Pub, Gastropub, Sports Bar
**Average price:** Modest
**Area:** North Inner City
**Address:**129 Capel St Dublin 1
**Phone:** 353 1 8746844

#205
**Crowe's Public House**
**Category:** Pub
**Average price:** Modest
**Area:** Ballsbridge
**Address:**10 Merrion Rd Dublin 4
**Phone:** 353 1 6680955

#206
**The Baggot Inn**
**Category:** Pub, Sports Bar, Cocktail Bar
**Average price:** Modest
**Area:** South Inner City
**Address:**143 Lower Baggot St Dublin 2
**Phone:** 353 1 6618758

#207
**The Cat & Cage**
**Category:** Pub
**Average price:** Modest
**Area:** Drumcondra
**Address:**74 Upper Drumcondra Rd
Dublin 9
**Phone:** 353 1 8573809

#208
**Sinnotts**
**Category:** Pub, Sports Bar, Gastropub
**Average price:** Modest
**Area:** South Inner City
**Address:**South King St Dublin 2
**Phone:** 353 1 4784698

#209
**Mourne Seafood Bar**
**Category:** Seafood, Bar
**Average price:** Expensive
**Area:** Grand Canal Dock
**Address:**Charlotte Quay Dublin
**Phone:** 353 1 6688862

#210
**Taylor's Three Rock Restaurant**
**Category:** Cabaret, Irish, Music Venue
**Area:** Kilmashogue
**Address:**Orange Rd Dublin 16
**Phone:** 353 1 4942311

#211
**Gaffney & Son**
**Category:** Pub
**Area:** Marino
**Address:**5 Fairview Dublin 3
**Phone:** 353 1 8339803

#212
**MacTurcaills**
**Category:** Pub
**Average price:** Modest
**Area:** South Inner City
**Address:**15 15 Townsend St Dublin 2
**Phone:** 353 1 6790981

#213
**The Clarendon**
**Category:** Pub, Gastropub
**Average price:** Modest
**Area:** South Inner City
**Address:**4 Chatham Row Dublin 2
**Phone:** 353 1 6170060

#214
**Harry's On The Green**
**Category:** Bar, American
**Average price:** Modest
**Area:** South Inner City
**Address:**2 Kings St South Dublin 2
**Phone:** 353 1 4758504

#215
**Break For The Border**
**Category:** Pub, Gastropub
**Average price:** Modest
**Area:** South Inner City
**Address:**Lower Stephens St Dublin 2
**Phone:** 353 1 4781190

#216
**Madigans**
**Category:** Pub
**Average price:** Modest
**Area:** North Inner City
**Address:**19 Lower O'Connell St Dublin 1
**Phone:** 353 1 8743692

#217
**Cusacks Spinnaker**
**Category:** Pub
**Area:** North Strand
**Address:**145 N Strand Rd Dublin 3
**Phone:** 353 1 8741417

#218
**Turks Head**
**Category:** Pub, Dance Club, Gastropub
**Average price:** Modest
**Area:** Temple Bar
**Address:**27 Parliament St Dublin 2
**Phone:** 353 1 6799701

#219
**Lord Edward Seafood Restaurant**
**Category:** Pub, Seafood
**Average price:** Modest
**Area:** Clanbrassil St
**Address:**23 Christchurch Pl Dublin 8
**Phone:** 353 1 4542420

#220
**Slipper**
**Category:** Pub
**Average price:** Inexpensive
**Area:** Glasnevin
**Address:**125 Ballymun Rd Dublin 9
**Phone:** 353 1 8570114

#221
**Frank Ryan & Son**
**Category:** Pub, Dive Bar
**Average price:** Modest
**Area:** Smithfield
**Address:**5 Queen St Dublin 7
**Phone:** 353 1 8725204

#222
**Paddy Cullen Public House**
**Category:** Pub
**Average price:** Modest
**Area:** Ballsbridge
**Address:**14 Merrion Rd Dublin 4
**Phone:** 353 1 6684492

#223
**Hartigan's**
**Category:** Pub
**Average price:** Modest
**Area:** South Inner City
**Address:**100 Leeson St Lower Dublin 2
**Phone:** 353 1 6762280

#224
**The Horseshow House**
**Category:** Pub, Sports Bar
**Average price:** Modest
**Area:** Ballsbridge
**Address:**34 Merrion Rd Dublin 4
**Phone:** 353 1 6689424

#225
**Flannerys**
**Category:** Pub
**Average price:** Modest
**Area:** Harcourt
**Address:**6 Camden St Lower Dublin 2
**Phone:** 353 1 4782238

#226
**The Mint Bar**
**Category:** Pub, Champagne Bar
**Average price:** Expensive
**Area:** South Inner City
**Address:**Westmoreland St Dublin 2
**Phone:** 353 1 6451322

#227
**The Hungry Mexican Restaurant**
**Category:** Mexican, Bar
**Average price:** Modest
**Area:** Bolton St
**Address:**57 Bolton St Dublin 1
**Phone:** 353 1 5480126

#228
**The Dropping Well**
**Category:** Pub, Gastropub, Lounge
**Average price:** Modest
**Area:** Milltown
**Address:**Milltown Rd Dublin 6
**Phone:** 353 1 4973969

#229
**Dandelion**
**Category:** Bar, Dance Club, Irish
**Average price:** Modest
**Area:** South Inner City
**Address:**130 St Stephen's Green Dublin 2
**Phone:** 353 1 460870

#230
**The Patriot Inn**
**Category:** Pub
**Average price:** Inexpensive
**Area:** Island Bridge
**Address:**760 South Circular Rd Dublin 8
**Phone:** 353 1 6799595

#231
**Celt Pub**
**Category:** Pub
**Average price:** Modest
**Area:** North Inner City
**Address:**81 Talbot St Dublin 1
**Phone:** 353 1 8788855

#232
**Stil**
**Category:** Pub
**Average price:** Expensive
**Area:** Phone number
**Address:**Charlemont Pl Dublin 2
**Phone:** 353 1 4029988

#233
**Trinity Bar and Venue**
**Category:** Sports Bar
**Average price:** Modest
**Area:** South Inner City
**Address:**46-49 Dame St Dublin 2
**Phone:** 353 1 6794455

#234
**The Black Door**
**Category:** Jazz & Blues, Music Venues
**Area:** Harcourt
**Address:**58 Harcourt St Dublin 2
**Phone:** 353 1 4764606

#235
**O'Dwyers Pub Kilmacud**
**Category:** Pub
**Average price:** Modest
**Area:** Kilmacud
**Address:**118 Kilmacud Rd Lower Dublin
**Phone:** 353 1 2882228

#236
**Smyth's**
**Category:** Pub
**Area:** Baggot St
**Address:**10 Haddington Rd Dublin 4
**Phone:** 353 1 6606305

#237
**The Grafton Lounge**
**Category:** Lounge
**Average price:** Modest
**Area:** South Inner City
**Address:**Upper Duke Ln Dublin 2
**Phone:** 353 1 6796260

#238
**The Village**
**Category:** Bar, Dance Club, Music Venues
**Average price:** Expensive
**Area:** South Inner City
**Address:**26 Wexford St Dublin 2
**Phone:** 353 1 4760555

#239
**Arc Cafe Bar**
Category: Pub, Gastropub
Average price: Modest
Area: Palmerstown
Address:Liffey Valley SC
Fonthill Rd Dublin 22
Phone: 353 1 6207003

#240
**Laughter Lounge**
Category: Pub, Comedy Club
Average price: Expensive
Area: North Inner City
Address:Eden Quay Dublin 1
Phone: 353 1 8783003

#241
**Hanlon's**
Category: Pub
Average price: Modest
Area: Phone number
Address:N Circular Rd Dublin 7
Phone: 353 1 8385261

#242
**Ely Wine Bar**
Category: Breakfast & Brunch,
Wine Bar, European
Average price: Modest
Area: South Inner City
Address:22 Ely Place Dublin 2
Phone: 353 1 6768986

#243
**Comet**
Category: Pub
Average price: Modest
Area: Whitehall
Address:243 - 245 Swords Rd Dublin
Phone: 353 1 8424986

#244
**Coach House**
Category: Pub
Area: Ballinteer
Address:Ballinteer Avenue Dublin 16
Phone: 353 1 2987088

#245
**Lafayette Café Bar**
Category: Dance Club, Bar
Average price: Modest
Area: South Inner City
Address:22-25 Westmoreland St Dublin 2
Phone: 353 1 6746335

#246
**The Good Bits**
Category: Dance Club, Music Venues
Average price: Modest
Area: Gardiner St
Address:Store St Dublin 1
Phone: 353 86 8262303

#247
**Hemidemisemi Quaverbar**
Category: Bar
Average price: Modest
Area: Phone number
Address:Point Village Dublin 1
Phone: 353 1 4338830

#248
**Harry Byrnes Pub**
Category: Pub
Average price: Modest
Area: Clontarf
Address:107 Howth Rd Dublin 3
Phone: 353 1 8332650

#249
**Bellamy's Lounge Bar**
Category: Pub
Average price: Modest
Area: Ballsbridge
Address:13 Ballsbridge Terrace Dublin 4
Phone: 353 1 6680397

#250
**The Wellington**
Category: Pub
Area: Baggot St
Address:1a Upper Baggot St Dublin 4
Phone: 353 1 6607344

#251
**The Lotts Café Bar**
Category: Gastropub, Pub, Jazz & Blues
Average price: Modest
Area: North Inner City
Address:9 Lower Liffey St Dublin 1
Phone: 353 1 8727669

#252
**Russells**
Category: Pub, Music Venues
Average price: Modest
Area: Phone number
Address:60 Ranelagh Rd Dublin 6
Phone: 353 1 4977120

#253
**Krystle**
Category: Dance Club
Average price: Expensive
Area: Harcourt
Address:21-25 Harcourt St Dublin 2
Phone: 353 87 6745393

#254
**Crowbar**
Category: Cocktail Bar
Area: Temple Bar
Address:Curved St Dublin 2
Phone: 353 1 6709105

#255
**Fiorentina**
Category: Italian, Cocktail Bar
Average price: Expensive
Area: South Inner City
Address:40 Parliament St Dublin 2
Phone: 353 1 6351922

#256
**Robert Reade**
Category: Pub
Average price: Modest
Area: Gardiner St
Address:19 Store St Dublin 1
Phone: 353 1 8559992

#257
**Block T**
Category: Music Venues
Area: Smithfield
Address:1-6 Haymarket Dublin 7
Phone: 353 1 5351014

#258
**Tommy O'Gara's**
Category: Pub
Average price: Modest
Area: Stoneybatter
Address:19 Stoneybatter Dublin 7
Phone: 353 1 6778178

#259
**The Cherry Tree**
Category: Pub
Area: Bluebell
Address:Walkinstown Roundabout Dublin
Phone: 353 1 4503983

#260
**O'Sullivan's Bar**
Category: Bar
Average price: Modest
Area: Temple Bar
Address:10 Westmoreland St Dublin 2
Phone: 353 1 6708133

#261
**KC Peaches Wine Cave**
Category: Wine Bar, Cafe
Average price: Modest
Area: South Inner City
Address:28-29 Nassau St Dublin 2
Phone: 353 1 6336872

#262
**O' Donoghues**
Category: Pub, Irish
Average price: Modest
Area: South Inner City
Address:15 Suffolk St Dublin 2
Phone: 353 1 6770605

#263
**The Palace Nightclub**
Category: Pool Hall, Bar
Average price: Modest
Area: Harcourt
Address:84/87 Lower Camden St Dublin 2
Phone: 353 1 4780808

#264
**Madigans**
Category: Pub
Average price: Modest
Area: North Inner City
Address:25 N Earl St Dublin 1
Phone: 353 1 8740646

#265
**The Bachelor Inn**
Category: Pub
Average price: Modest
Area: North Inner City
Address:31 Batchelors Walk Dublin 1
Phone: 353 1 8731238

#266
**Lagoona**
Category: Pub
Average price: Modest
Area: IFSC
Address:Unit 1, Custom House
Square Dublin 1
Phone: 353 1 7918928

#267
**Enoteca Delle Langhe**
**Category:** Italian, Wine Bar
**Average price:** Modest
**Area:** North Inner City
**Address:**Blooms Lane Dublin 1
**Phone:** 353 1 8880834

#268
**An Poitin Stil**
**Category:** Irish, Pub
**Average price:** Modest
**Area:** Rathcoole
**Address:**Naas Rd Dublin
**Phone:** 353 1 4589244

#269
**The Parnell Heritage Pub & Grill**
**Category:** Sports Bar, Gastropub,
Cocktail Bar
**Average price:** Modest
**Area:** North Inner City
**Address:**72-74 Parnell St Dublin 1
**Phone:** 353 1 8783380

#270
**The Eden House**
**Category:** Pub
**Average price:** Modest
**Area:** Rathfarnham
**Address:**Grange Rd Dublin 16
**Phone:** 353 1 4931492

#271
**Millenium Bar**
**Category:** Pub
**Average price:** Inexpensive
**Area:** Arbour Hill
**Address:**5 Parkgate St Dublin 8
**Phone:** 353 1 6795644

#272
**Windjammer**
**Category:** Pub
**Average price:** Modest
**Area:** South Inner City
**Address:**111 Townsend St Dublin 2
**Phone:** 353 1 6772576

#273
**Ryans**
**Category:** Pub
**Average price:** Inexpensive
**Area:** Harcourt
**Address:**92 Camden St Lower Dublin 2
**Phone:** 353 1 4753528

#274
**Leggs**
**Category:** Wine Bar, Dance Club
**Average price:** Modest
**Area:** Harcourt
**Address:**29 Lower Leeson St Dublin 2
**Phone:** 353 1 6766269

#275
**The Exchequer Winebar**
**Category:** Wine Bar
**Average price:** Expensive
**Area:** Rathgar
**Address:**19 Ranelagh Dublin 6
**Phone:** 353 1 4215780

#276
**Lillies Bordello**
**Category:** Dance Club
**Average price:** Expensive
**Area:** South Inner City
**Address:**Adam Court Dublin 2
**Phone:** 353 1 6799204

#277
**Graces**
**Category:** Pub
**Average price:** Modest
**Area:** Rathmines
**Address:**2 Rathgar Rd Dublin 6
**Phone:** 353 1 4974345

#278
**Lighthouse Bar**
**Category:** Pub
**Area:** Howth
**Address:**2 Church St Dublin
**Phone:** 353 1 8322827

#279
**Downeys**
**Category:** Pub
**Area:** Grange Castle
**Address:**Grange Cross Dublin 10
**Phone:** 353 1 6264679

#280
**The Blue Haven**
**Category:** Pub
**Average price:** Modest
**Area:** Rathfarnham
**Address:**1A Ballyroan Rd Dublin 16
**Phone:** 353 1 4945382

#281
**Blarney Inn**
**Category:** Irish, Pub
**Average price:** Modest
**Area:** South Inner City
**Address:**47- 49 Kildare St Dublin 2
**Phone:** 353 1 6794388

#282
**Darkey Kellys**
**Category:** Pub, Irish
**Average price:** Inexpensive
**Area:** Wood Quay
**Address:**Copper Alley, Fishamble St
Dublin 8
**Phone:** 353 1 6796500

#283
**The Epicenter- Venue Bar**
**Category:** Pub, Irish
**Average price:** Modest
**Area:** Marino
**Address:**Eastpoint Business Park
Dublin 3
**Phone:** 353 1 8750101

#284
**Sin**
**Category:** Dance Club
**Average price:** Expensive
**Area:** Temple Bar
**Address:**17-19 Sycamore St Dublin 2
**Phone:** 353 1 6334232

#285
**Vanilla Nightclub**
**Category:** Dance Club
**Area:** Rathgar
**Address:**19-29 Morehampton Rd Dublin 4
**Phone:** 353 87 4174877

#286
**Club M Nightclub**
**Category:** Dance Club
**Average price:** Modest
**Area:** Temple Bar
**Address:**Anglesea St Dublin 2
**Phone:** 353 1 6715485

#287
**Searsons Public House**
**Category:** Pub
**Average price:** Modest
**Area:** Baggot St
**Address:**42 Upper Baggot St Dublin 4
**Phone:** 353 1 6600330

#288
**The Seabank House**
**Category:** Pub
**Area:** East Wall
**Address:**123 E Wall Rd Dublin 3
**Phone:** 353 1 8560095

#289
**Black Pig**
**Category:** Ethnic Food, Wine Bar
**Area:** Milltown
**Address:**95B Morehampton Rd Dublin 4
**Phone:** 353 1 6674828

#290
**P. McCormack and Sons**
**Category:** Pub, Irish
**Area:** Monkstown
**Address:**67 Lower Mountown Rd Dublin
**Phone:** 353 1 2805519

#291
**Brock Inn**
**Category:** Pub
**Average price:** Modest
**Area:** Phone number
**Address:**Ashbourne Rd Dublin 11
**Phone:** 353 1 8342216

#292
**The Pint Bar & Venue**
**Category:** Pub, Dance Club
**Average price:** Modest
**Area:** North Inner City
**Address:**28 Eden Quay Dublin 1
**Phone:** 353 1 8745255

#293
**M Hughes**
**Category:** Pub
**Area:** Four Courts
**Address:**19 Chancery St Dublin 7
**Phone:** 353 1 8726540

#294
**Cocoon**
**Category:** Bar
**Area:** South Inner City
**Address:**Unit 2 Royal Hibernian Way
Daws Dublin 3
**Phone:** 353 1 6796259

#295
**The Underground**
**Category:** Dance Club
**Average price:** Inexpensive
**Area:** Phone number
**Address:**30-32 Westland Row Dublin 2
**Phone:** 353 1 6611124

#296
**Browns Barn**
**Category:** Gastropub, Cocktail Bar
**Area:** Bluebell
**Address:**Naas Rd Dublin 12
**Phone:** 353 1 4640999

#297
**Old Mill Pub**
**Category:** Pub
**Area:** Bohernabreena
**Address:**Old Bawn Rd Dublin 24
**Phone:** 353 1 4515991

#298
**Oil Can Harrys**
**Category:** Brasserie, Pub
**Average price:** Modest
**Area:** Baggot St
**Address:**31 Lower Mount St Dublin 2
**Phone:** 353 1 6611828

#299
**O'Neills Victorian Pub
& Townhouse**
**Category:** Pub, Bed & Breakfast
**Average price:** Modest
**Area:** South Inner City
**Address:**36- 37 Pearse St Dublin 2
**Phone:** 353 1 6714074

#300
**Man O' War**
**Category:** Pub
**Area:** Skerries
**Address:**Courtlough Dublin
**Phone:** 353 1 8415528

#301
**Whiskey Palace
@ The Palace Bar**
**Category:** Cocktail Bar, Pub
**Area:** Temple Bar
**Address:**21 Fleet St Dublin 2
**Phone:** 353 1 6717388

#302
**Chaplins Bar**
**Category:** Pub
**Average price:** Inexpensive
**Area:** South Inner City
**Address:**2 Hawkins St Dublin 2
**Phone:** 353 1 6775225

#303
**King 7**
**Category:** Dance Club, Karaoke
**Area:** North Inner City
**Address:**122 Capel St Dublin 1
**Phone:** 353 1 8788988

#304
**Mary's Bar**
**Category:** Pub
**Average price:** Modest
**Area:** South Inner City
**Address:**8 Wicklow St Dublin 2
**Phone:** 353 1 6708629

#305
**Mother Kellys**
**Category:** Pub
**Area:** Gardiner St
**Address:**74 Talbot St Dublin 1
**Phone:** 353 1 8366882

#306
**Mcgettigans Cookhouse
& Bar Restaurant**
**Category:** Bar, Steakhouse
**Average price:** Modest
**Area:** Gardiner St
**Address:**Amiens St Dublin 1
**Phone:** 353 1 8559638

#307
**The Den Bar**
**Category:** Pub
**Average price:** Modest
**Area:** Baggot St
**Address:**27/29 Pembroke Rd Dublin 4
**Phone:** 353 1 6682522

#308
**Smyths of Fairview**
**Category:** Pub
**Area:** Marino
**Address:**12 Fairview Dublin 3
**Phone:** 353 1 8332767

#309
**The Boom Boom Room**
**Category:** Music Venues
**Area:** Phone number
**Address:**70 Parnell St Dublin 1
**Phone:** 353 1 8732687

#310
**The Ruby Sessions**
**Category:** Jazz & Blues, Music Venues
**Average price:** Inexpensive
**Area:** Phone number
**Address:**9 College St Dublin 1
**Phone:** 353 1 671061

#311
**O'Sheas Clonskeagh House**
**Category:** Pub
**Average price:** Modest
**Area:** Milltown
**Address:**68 Clonskeagh Rd Dublin 6
**Phone:** 353 1 2830189

#312
**Devitts**
**Category:** Pub
**Average price:** Inexpensive
**Area:** Harcourt
**Address:**78 Lower Camden St Dublin 2
**Phone:** 353 1 4753414

#313
**Bach 16**
**Category:** Mediterranean, Wine Bar
**Average price:** Modest
**Area:** North Inner City
**Address:**16 Bachelor's Walk Dublin 1
**Phone:** 353 1 8720215

#314
**Brunnigans**
**Category:** Pub
**Area:** North Inner City
**Address:**9 Cathedral St Dublin 1
**Phone:** 353 1 8740137

#315
**Club Lapello**
**Category:** Adult Entertainment
**Area:** South Inner City
**Address:**55 Dame St Dublin 3
**Phone:** 353 1 6790514

#316
**Mercadillo Temple Bar**
**Category:** Pub
**Area:** Temple Bar
**Address:**Plaza Temple Bar Dublin
**Phone:** 353 1 6708270

#317
**Killinarden House Sns**
**Category:** Pub, Bed & Breakfast
**Area:** South Inner City
**Address:**Ballyowen Palmerstown Dublin
**Phone:** 353 1 6268505

#318
**Sporting Emporium**
**Category:** Casino, Sports Bar
**Area:** South Inner City
**Address:**Anne's Lane Dublin 2
**Phone:** 353 1 7030600

#319
**The Lord Mayor's Lounge**
**Category:** Lounge
**Average price:** Expensive
**Area:** South Inner City
**Address:**27 St Stephen's Green Dublin 2
**Phone:** 353 1 6634500

#320
**Generator Laughs Comedy**
**Category:** Comedy Club
**Area:** Smithfield
**Address:**Smithfield Square Dublin 7
**Phone:** 353 1 9010222

#321
**The Liberty Belle**
**Category:** Pub
**Area:** The Liberties
**Address:**33 Francis St Dublin 8
**Phone:** 353 1 4542638

#322
**Bermingham's**
**Category:** Pub
**Average price:** Inexpensive
**Area:** Phibsboro
**Address:**111 Lower Dorset St Dublin 1
**Phone:** 353 1 8305083

#323
**Pimlico Tavern**
**Category:** Pub
**Area:** Cork St
**Address:**61 Pimlico Dublin 8
**Phone:** 353 1 4530867

#324
**Arthur Mayne's**
**Category:** Pub
**Average price:** Modest
**Area:** Ballsbridge
**Address:**48 Donnybrook Rd Dublin 4
**Phone:** 353 1 2187869

#325
**Karaoke Taxi**
**Category:** Karaoke, Local Flavor
**Area:** Phone number
**Address:**Dublin
**Phone:** 353 86 2213425

#326
**Planet Murphy's**
**Category:** Sports Bar, Pool Hall
**Average price:** Modest
**Area:** Harcourt
**Address:**84 - 87 Lower Camden St
Dublin 2
**Phone:** 353 1 4780808

#327
**TGI Fridays**
**Category:** Bar, American, Burgers
**Average price:** Expensive
**Area:** Temple Bar
**Address:**St Stephens Green Shopping
Centre Dublin 2
**Phone:** 353 1 4781233

#328
**Kavanaghs Marino House**
**Category:** Pub, Irish
**Average price:** Inexpensive
**Area:** Clontarf
**Address:**16 Malahide Rd Dublin 3
**Phone:** 353 1 8332786

#329
**Peacock's Steakhouse**
**Category:** Steakhouse, Pub
**Average price:** Modest
**Area:** Phone number
**Address:**Rivervalley Shopping Centre
**Phone:** 353 1 8408969

#330
**McCloskeys**
**Category:** Pub
**Average price:** Modest
**Area:** Milltown
**Address:**83 Morehampton Rd Dublin 4
**Phone:** 353 1 6684345

#331
**Seamus Ennis Cultural Centre**
**Category:** Music Venues
**Area:** Garristown
**Address:**The Naul Dublin 1
**Phone:** 353 1 8020898

#332
**Dollymount House**
**Category:** Pub
**Area:** Clontarf
**Address:**Clontarf Rd Dublin 3
**Phone:** 353 1 8331483

#333
**The Goblet**
**Category:** Pub, Gastropub
**Area:** Clarehall
**Address:**Malahide Rd Dublin 5
**Phone:** 353 1 8327311

#334
**Sean O'Casey**
**Category:** Pub
**Area:** North Inner City
**Address:**105 Marlborough St Dublin 1
**Phone:** 353 1 8744294

#335
**The Watermill**
**Category:** Pub
**Average price:** Modest
**Area:** Raheny
**Address:**411 Howth Rd Dublin 5
**Phone:** 353 1 8319574

#336
**Alfie Byrne's**
**Category:** Pub
**Average price:** Modest
**Area:** Harcourt
**Address:**Earlsfort Terrace Dublin 2
**Phone:** 353 1 6028900

#337
**Club 92**
**Category:** Dance Club
**Average price:** Modest
**Area:** Leopardstown
**Address:**Leopardstown Racecourse
Dublin 18
**Phone:** 353 1 2895686

#338
**TGI Fridays**
**Category:** American, Burgers, Lounge
**Average price:** Modest
**Area:** Dundrum
**Address:**Dundrum Town Centre Dublin 16
**Phone:** 353 1 2987299

#339
**ThinkTank**
**Category:** Dance Club
**Average price:** Modest
**Area:** Temple Bar
**Address:**24 Eustace St Dublin 2
**Phone:** 353 86 8067145

#340
**Tramco**
**Category:** Pub, Dance Club
**Average price:** Modest
**Area:** Rathmines
**Address:**121 Lower Rathmines Rd
Dublin 6
**Phone:** 353 1 4968049

#341
**Isaac Butt Bar**
**Category:** Pub, Gastropub
**Area:** IFSC
**Address:**1 Store St Dublin 1
**Phone:** 353 1 8197635

#342
**Wrens Nest**
**Category:** Pub
**Average price:** Modest
**Area:** Phone number
**Address:**Strawberry Beds Dublin 20
**Phone:** 353 1 8699009

#343
**Silver Granite**
**Category:** Pub
**Average price:** Modest
**Area:** Ballyfermot
**Address:**Kennels Fort Rd Dublin 20
**Phone:** 353 1 6264050

#344
**Terenure Inn**
**Category:** Pub
**Average price:** Modest
**Area:** Terenure
**Address:**94-96 Terenure Rd N Dublin 6w
**Phone:** 353 1 4907552

#345
**Chancery Inn**
**Category:** Pub, Dive Bar
**Area:** Four Courts
**Address:**1 Inns Quay Dublin 7
**Phone:** 353 1 6770420

#346
**The Green Room**
**Category:** Gastropub, Pub
**Average price:** Modest
**Area:** Phone number
**Address:**Beside the O2 Arena Dublin 1
**Phone:** 353 1 8944888

#347
**Fillies Cafe Bar**
**Category:** Pub, Cafe
**Average price:** Modest
**Area:** Leopardstown
**Address:**Leopardstown Racecourse
Dublin 18
**Phone:** 353 1 6817200

#348
**Eamonn Rea's**
**Category:** Pub
**Area:** Arbour Hill
**Address:**25 Parkgate St Dublin 8
**Phone:** 353 1 6772738

#349
**Toddy's Bar**
**Category:** Pub
**Average price:** Modest
**Area:** North Inner City
**Address:**23 Upper O'Connell St Dublin 1
**Phone:** 353 1 8746881

#350
**C Central Bar**
**Category:** Pub
**Area:** Rotunda
**Address:**Camden St Dublin 2
**Phone:** 353 1 4759666

#351
**Magic Carpet**
**Category:** Pub, Gastropub
**Area:** Phone number
**Address:**Cornelcourt Village Dublin 18
**Phone:** 353 1 2897257

#352
**Karma**
**Category:** Pub, Chinese
**Area:** Phone number
**Address:**16-18 Fishamble St Dublin 2
**Phone:** 353 1 16709400

#353
**The Song Room**
**Category:** Bar, Music Venues
**Area:** Lucan
**Address:**11 S Great Georges St Dublin 2
**Phone:** 353 1 6711220

#354
**Leonard Corner Cafe Bar**
**Category:** Coffee & Tea, Pub
**Average price:** Modest
**Area:** Rialto
**Address:**117 S Circular Rd Dublin 7
**Phone:** 353 1 4542332

#355
**Dublin Wine Room**
**Category:** Irish, Seafood, Wine Bar
**Average price:** Modest
**Area:** IFSC
**Address:**Custom House Square Dublin 1
**Phone:** 353 1 6360616

#356
**The Cornerstone**
**Category:** Pub
**Average price:** Inexpensive
**Area:** South Inner City
**Address:**40 Wexford St Dublin 2
**Phone:** 353 1 4789816

#357
**Buck Whaleys**
**Category:** Dance Club
**Average price:** Expensive
**Area:** South Inner City
**Address:**67 Lower Leeson St Dublin 2
**Phone:** 353 1 6334200

#358
**Lower Deck**
**Category:** Pub
**Average price:** Modest
**Area:** Harcourt
**Address:**1 Portobello Harbour Dublin 8
**Phone:** 353 1 4751423

#359
**Mary Mac's**
**Category:** Pub
**Average price:** Modest
**Area:** Ballsbridge
**Address:**12 Merrion Rd Dublin 4
**Phone:** 353 1 6694492

#360
**The Galway Hooker**
**Category:**Bar
**Average price:** Modest
**Area:** Phone number
**Address:**Heuston Station Dublin 8
**Phone:** 353 1 6703463

#361
**Ballinteer House**
**Category:** Guest Houses, Bar
**Area:** Ballinteer
**Address:**Superquinn Shopping Ctr Ballinteer
Avenue Dublin 16
**Phone:** 353 1 2989600

#362
**The Grasshopper Inn**
**Category:** Irish, Pub
**Area:** Phone number
**Address:**Clonee Dublin 15
**Phone:** 353 1 8251049

#363
**Brannigans**
**Category:** Pub, Irish
**Area:** North Inner City
**Address:**9 Cathedral St Dublin 1
**Phone:** 353 1 8740137

#364
**Piccolo**
**Category:** Wine Bar, Italian
**Average price:** Modest
**Area:** Temple Bar
**Address:**4 Lower Exchange St Dublin 1
**Phone:** 353 1 6799271

#365
**Kildare St. Hotel**
**Category:** Hotel, Pub
**Area:** South Inner City
**Address:**47 - 49 Kildare St Dublin 2
**Phone:** 353 1 6794643

#366
**The Irish House Party**
**Category:** Music Venues, Irish
**Area:** The Liberties
**Address:**19 Francis St Dublin 8
**Phone:** 353 1 6618410

#367
**Racecourse Inn**
**Category:** Pub
**Average price:** Modest
**Area:** Phone number
**Address:**Racecourse SC Grange Rd
Dublin 13
**Phone:** 353 1 8391816

#368
**The Pier Inn**
**Category:** Pub
**Average price:** Inexpensive
**Area:** Dún Laoghaire
**Address:**88 Lower Georges St Dublin
**Phone:** 353 1 2300760

#369
**Kielys Mount Merrion**
**Category:** Pub
**Area:** Mount Merrion
**Address:**68 Deerpark Rd Dublin
**Phone:** 353 1 2832204

#370
**The East Point Cafe Bar & Venue**
**Category:** Sports Bar
**Average price:** Modest
**Area:** Phone number
**Address:**East Point Business Park
Dublin 3
**Phone:** 353 1 8750101

#371
**The Velvet Room**
**Category:** Dance Club
**Average price:** Modest
**Area:** Rotunda
**Address:**Great Denmark St Dublin 1
**Phone:** 353 1 8737700

#372
**Ferryman Inn**
**Category:** Pub
**Average price:** Modest
**Area:** Grand Canal Dock
**Address:**35 Sir John Rogerson Quay
Dublin 2
**Phone:** 353 1 6717053

#373
**Fitzsimons Bar & Nightclub**
**Category:** Wine Bar, European,
Dance Club
**Average price:** Modest
**Area:** Temple Bar
**Address:**21-22 Wellington Quay Dublin 2
**Phone:** 353 1 6779315

#374
**The Tram**
**Category:** Pub
**Area:** James' St
**Address:**131 James St Dublin 3
**Phone:** 353 1 6779700

#375
**Ambassador Theatre**
**Category:** Performing Arts,
Music Venues, Museum
**Area:** North Inner City
**Address:**O'Connell St Dublin 1
**Phone:** 353 818 333773

#376
**Auld Triangle**
**Category:** Pub
**Average price:** Inexpensive
**Area:** Mountjoy
**Address:**28 Lower Dorset St Dublin 1
**Phone:** 353 1 8363378

#377
**Beaumont House**
**Category:** Pub
**Average price:** Modest
**Area:** Beaumont
**Address:**1 Shantalla Rd Dublin 9
**Phone:** 353 1 8371353

#378
**Bodkins**
**Category:** Pub
**Average price:** Modest
**Area:** Bolton St
**Address:**57 Bolton St Dublin 1
**Phone:** 353 1 8730128

#379
**Pifko**
**Category:** Gastropub
**Average price:** Inexpensive
**Area:** Thomas St
**Address:**41-43 Ushers Quay Dublin 8
**Phone:** 353 1 5152087

#380
**Murphys Pub**
**Category:** Pub
**Average price:** Modest
**Area:** Rathgar
**Address:**93 Upper Rathmines Dublin 6
**Phone:** 353 1 4967707

#381
**RDS Simmonscourt**
**Category:** Venues, Music Venues
**Average price:** Modest
**Area:** Phone number
**Address:**Ballsbridge Dublin 4
**Phone:** 353 1 6680866

#382
**Bradys Castleknock Inn**
**Category:** Pub
**Average price:** Modest
**Area:** Blanchardstown
**Address:**Old Navan Rd Dublin 15
**Phone:** 353 1 8203966

#383
**Joxer Dalys**
**Category:** Pub
**Area:** Inns Quay
**Address:**103 Upper Dorset St Dublin 1
**Phone:** 353 1 0005049

#384
**Mortons**
**Category:** Lounge
**Average price:** Modest
**Area:** Firhouse
**Address:**Firhouse Rd Dublin 24
**Phone:** 353 1 4946361

#385
**Traffic**
**Category:** Bar
**Area:** North Inner City
**Address:**54 Middle Abbey St Dublin
**Phone:** 353 1 8734800

#386
**Knightsbridge Bar**
**Category:** Pub
**Area:** North Inner City
**Address:**23 25 Bachelors Walk Dublin 1
**Phone:** 353 1 8049174

#387
**Batchelor Inn**
**Category:** Pub
**Area:** North Inner City
**Address:**31 Batchelors Walk Dublin 1
**Phone:** 353 1 8731238

#388
**Madigans**
**Category:** Pub
**Average price:** Modest
**Area:** North Inner City
**Address:**4 Lower Abbey St Dublin 1
**Phone:** 353 1 8745456

#389
**Brewery Lane**
**Category:** Bar
**Area:** Temple Bar
**Address:**Wellington Quay Dublin 2
**Phone:** 353 1 6074010

#390
**Ned Keenan's Irish Music Bar**
**Category:** Pub
**Average price:** Inexpensive
**Area:** North Inner City
**Address:**75 Lower Gardiner St Dublin 1
**Phone:** 353 1 8555442

#391
**Viva Bar & Cafe**
**Category:** Pub
**Area:** South Inner City
**Address:**52 Sth William St Dublin
**Phone:** 353 1 6770212

#392
**Magic Glasses**
**Category:** Bar, Bistro
**Area:** South Inner City
**Address:**O'Callaghan Stephen's Green Hotel
Dublin 2
**Phone:** 353 1 6073600

#393
**Voodoo Lounge**
**Category:** Lounge
**Average price:** Inexpensive
**Area:** Smithfield
**Address:**40 Arran Quay Dublin 7
**Phone:** 353 1 8736013

#394
**Anseo Comedy Club**
**Category:** Comedy Club
**Average price:** Inexpensive
**Area:** Harcourt
**Address:**18 Camden St Dublin 2
**Phone:** 353 86 0774119

#395
**Hynes Pub**
**Category:** Pub
**Area:** Grangegorman
**Address:**79 Prussia St Dublin 2
**Phone:** 353 1 8681005

#396
**Flanigans**
**Category:** Pub
**Area:** Rathmines
**Address:**161 Harolds Cross Rd Dublin 6w
**Phone:** 353 1 4972445

#397
**Jodamis Bar**
**Category:** Pub, Active Life
**Average price:** Inexpensive
**Area:** Phone number
**Address:**Leopardstown Racecourse
Dublin 18
**Phone:** 353 1 2897699

#398
**O'Briens Bar**
**Category:** Pub
**Area:** Phone number
**Address:**8-9 Sussex Terrace Leeson St
Dublin 4
**Phone:** 353 1 6682594

#399
**Dublin City Pub Crawl**
**Category:** Pub
**Area:** Phone number
**Address:**Dublin 2
**Phone:** 353 86 4020040

#400
**Gilbert & Wright Clontarf**
**Category:** Irish, Pub
**Area:** Clontarf
**Address:**Hollybrook Park Dublin 3
**Phone:** 353 1 8338899

#401
**The Submarine**
**Category:** Pub
**Area:** Crumlin
**Address:**Cromwellsfort Rd Dublin 12
**Phone:** 353 1 4556074

#402
**Halfway House**
**Category:** Pub
**Area:** Walkinstown
**Address:**Walkinstown Rd Dublin 12
**Phone:** 353 1 4298518

#403
**Drury Buildings**
**Category:** Cocktail Bar, Irish
**Average price:** Modest
**Area:** South Inner City
**Address:**52-55 Drury St Dublin 2
**Phone:** 353 1 9602095

#404
**Madonna's Night Club**
**Category:** Dance Club
**Average price:** Modest
**Area:** Temple Bar
**Address:**3a Crown Alley Dublin 2
**Phone:** 353 87 7532926

#405
**Graingers**
**Category:** Pub
**Average price:** Modest
**Area:** Clontarf
**Address:**74 Malahide Rd Dublin 3
**Phone:** 353 1 8332794

#406
**Kobra Bar & Restaurant**
**Category:** European, Wine Bar
**Average price:** Modest
**Area:** Phone number
**Address:**26 Lower Leeson St Dublin 2
**Phone:** 353 1 6763380

#407
**Cumiskey's**
**Category:** Pub
**Average price:** Modest
**Area:** Navan Rd
**Address:**Blackhorse Avenue Dublin 7
**Phone:** 353 1 8381609

#408
**The Deadmans Inn**
**Category:** Pub
**Average price:** Expensive
**Area:** Rotunda
**Address:**Curtis Stream Lucan Rd
Dublin 20
**Phone:** 353 1 6265466

#409
**Graingers**
**Category:** Pub
**Area:** IFSC
**Address:**51 Talbot St Dublin 1
**Phone:** 353 1 8363249

#410
**Glimmer Man**
**Category:** Pub
**Average price:** Modest
**Area:** Stoneybatter
**Address:**14/15 Stoneybatter Dublin 7
**Phone:** 353 1 6774560

#411
**O'Maras Red Parrot**
**Category:** Pub
**Average price:** Inexpensive
**Area:** Ballybough
**Address:**57 Lower Dorset St Dublin 1
**Phone:** 353 1 8556310

#412
**The Hill Pub**
**Category:** Bar
**Area:** Rathmines
**Address:**Mount Pleasant Dublin 6
**Phone:** 353 1 4972156

#413
**Ciss Madden's**
**Category:** Pub
**Average price:** Modest
**Area:** Ballsbridge
**Address:**22-24 Donnybrook Rd Dublin 4
**Phone:** 353 1 2000209

#414
**Branagan's Bar**
**Category:** Pub
**Average price:** Modest
**Area:** Phone number
**Address:**Merrion Rd Dublin 4
**Phone:** 353 1 2694666

#415
**Two Sisters**
**Category:** Pub
**Average price:** Modest
**Area:** Kimmage
**Address:**6 Wainsfort Drive Dublin 6w
**Phone:** 353 1 4900166

#416
**Vertigo Bar**
**Category:** Lounge
**Average price:** Modest
**Area:** Grand Canal Dock
**Address:**2 Sir John Rogerson's Quay
Dublin 2
**Phone:** 353 1 6439500

#417
**Eleanora Lounge**
**Category:** Pub
**Area:** Drimnagh
**Address:**Drimnagh Rd Dublin 12
**Phone:** 353 1 4557928

#418
**The Villager**
**Category:** Pub
**Average price:** Inexpensive
**Area:** Chapelizod
**Address:**31 Main St Dublin 20
**Phone:** 353 1 6261766

#419
**Bridge Inn**
**Category:** Pub
**Area:** Chapelizod
**Address:**1 St Laurences Rd Dublin 20
**Phone:** 353 1 6264622

#420
**McDaids**
**Category:** Pub
**Average price:** Inexpensive
**Area:** South Inner City
**Address:**3 Harry St Dublin 2
**Phone:** 353 1 6794395

#421
**Ramble Inn**
**Category:** Pub
**Area:** Artane
**Address:**145 Killester Avenue Dublin 5
**Phone:** 353 1 8313005

#422
**Slattery's**
**Category:** Pub
**Average price:** Modest
**Area:** Beggars Bush
**Address:**62 Upper Grand Canal St
Dublin 4
**Phone:** 353 1 6685481

#423
**The Vathouse Bar**
**Category:** Pub
**Average price:** Modest
**Area:** Temple Bar
**Address:**6 Anglesea St Dublin 2
**Phone:** 353 1 6715622

#424
**Alchemy Club & Venue**
**Category:** Dance Club
**Average price:** Modest
**Area:** Temple Bar
**Address:**13-17 Fleet St Dublin 2
**Phone:** 353 86 6629575

#425
**Edenmore House**
**Category:** Pub
**Area:** Donaghmede
**Address:**Edenmore Avenue Dublin 5
**Phone:** 353 1 8478116

#426
**Cruisers Bar & Grill**
**Category:** Sports Bar, Gastropub
**Area:** Mulhuddart
**Address:**Tyrellstown Town Centre
Dublin 15
**Phone:** 353 1 8273784

#427
**The Old Boro**
**Category:** Pub
**Average price:** Modest
**Area:** Swords
**Address:**Main St Dublin
**Phone:** 353 1 8957445

#428
**The Vaults**
**Category:** Pub, Dance Club
**Average price:** Expensive
**Area:** IFSC
**Address:**Under Connolly Station Dublin 1
**Phone:** 353 1 6054700

#429
**Bar 52**
**Category:**Lounge
**Area:** North Inner City
**Address:**52 Middle Abbey St Dublin 1
**Phone:** 353 1 8728045

#430
**P McCormack & Sons**
**Category:** Pub
**Area:** South Inner City
**Address:**3 Burgh Quay Dublin 1
**Phone:** 353 1 8733121

#431
**Noo Bar**
**Category:** Bar
**Average price:** Modest
**Area:** South Inner City
**Address:**Duke Ln Dublin 2
**Phone:** 353 1 6796259

#432
**Voodoo Card Club**
**Category:** Adult Entertainment
**Area:** Smithfield
**Address:**39-40 Arran Quay Dublin 7
**Phone:** 353 1 8736013

#433
**Swiss Cottage**
**Category:** Pub
**Average price:** Modest
**Area:** Arbour Hill
**Address:**Swords St Dublin
**Phone:** 353 1 8428096

#434
**Flutes Wine Bar**
**Category:** Wine Bar
**Area:** Santry
**Address:**International Termainal Dublin
**Phone:** 353 1 8141111

#435
**Damson Diner**
**Category:** American, Asian Fusion
**Average price:** Modest
**Area:** South Inner City
**Address:**52 South William St Dublin 2
**Phone:** 353 1 6777007

#436
**Carr & O'Connell**
**Category:** Karaoke, Pub
**Area:** North Inner City
**Address:**30 Bachelors Walk Dublin 1
**Phone:** 353 1 8745730

#437
**Smith T P**
**Category:** Pub
**Average price:** Modest
**Area:** North Inner City
**Address:**9 Jervis St Dublin 1
**Phone:** 353 1 8782067

#438
**Briody's**
**Category:** Pub
**Area:** North Inner City
**Address:**97 Marlborough St Dublin 1
**Phone:** 353 1 8727016

#439
**Ned Kelly's Sportsclub & Casino**
**Category:** Casino, Pool Hall
**Area:** North Inner City
**Address:**43 Upper O' Connell St Dublin
**Phone:** 353 1 8732344

#440
**Gleesons**
**Category:** Pub
**Area:** South Inner City
**Address:**Dublin
**Phone:** 353 1 8174337

#441
**Rush Bar**
**Category:** Pub
**Average price:** Modest
**Area:** South Inner City
**Address:**65 South Williams St Dublin 2
**Phone:** 353 1 6719542

#442
**Madison Nightclub**
**Category:** Dance Club
**Average price:** Modest
**Area:** South Inner City
**Address:**6-8 Wicklow St Dublin 2
**Phone:** 353 86 4005998

#443
**Shakespear Pub**
**Category:** Pub
**Area:** Rotunda
**Address:**160 Parnell St Dublin 1
**Phone:** 353 1 8874527

#444
**Hill 16 Bar**
**Category:** Pub
**Area:** Rotunda
**Address:**Gardiner St Middle Dublin 1
**Phone:** 353 1 8744239

#445
**Tom Maye's**
**Category:** Pub
**Average price:** Modest
**Area:** Rotunda
**Address:**19a N Frederick St Dublin 1
**Phone:** 353 1 8746939

#446
**Delaneys**
**Category:** Pub
**Area:** Smithfield
**Address:**83 North King St Dublin 7
**Phone:** 353 1 8730824

#447
**The Clock**
**Category:** Pub
**Area:** Thomas St
**Address:**110 Thomas St Dublin 7
**Phone:** 353 1 6775563

#448
**Phil Ryan's**
**Category:** Pub
**Average price:** Inexpensive
**Area:** Mountjoy
**Address:**514 North Circular Rd Dublin 1
**Phone:** 353 1 8557838

#449
**Fountain Bar**
**Category:** Pub
**Average price:** Modest
**Area:** The Liberties
**Address:**61-63 Meath St Dublin 8
**Phone:** 353 1 4540260

#450
**Sunset House**
**Category:** Pub
**Area:** Ballybough
**Address:**1 Summerhill Parade Dublin 1
**Phone:** 353 1 8555573

#451
**Pembroke**
**Category:** Pub
**Average price:** Modest
**Area:** South Inner City
**Address:**31 Lower Pembroke St Dublin
**Phone:** 353 1 6762980

#452
**Harold House**
**Category:** Pub
**Area:** Portobello
**Address:**34 Clanbrassil St Upper Dublin 8
**Phone:** 353 1 4534529

#453
**Cross Bar**
**Category:** Pub, Gastropub
**Area:** Harold's Cross
**Address:**238 Harolds Cross Rd Dublin 6w
**Phone:** 353 1 4910346

#454
**Mother Red Caps**
**Category:** Pub
**Area:** Phone number
**Address:**Christchurch, Back lane Dublin 8
**Phone:** 353 1 4538306

#455
**KCR House Pub**
**Category:** Pub, Sports Bar, Lounge
**Average price:** Modest
**Area:** Terenure
**Address:**326 Kimmage Rd Lower Dublin
**Phone:** 353 1 4902530

#456
**Bradys Bar**
**Category:** Pub
**Average price:** Expensive
**Area:** Terenure
**Address:**5-9 Terenure Place Dublin 6
**Phone:** 353 1 4906424

#457
**Rodeo Joe's Nightclub &Bar**
**Category:** Bar
**Area:** Churchtown
**Address:**Braemor Rd Dublin 14
**Phone:** 353 1 2960411

#458
**The 79 Inn**
**Category:** Pub
**Area:** Ballyfermot
**Address:**79 Ballyfermot Rd Dublin 10
**Phone:** 353 1 6264994

#459
**Jack O'Rourke Public House**
**Category:** Pub
**Area:** Blackrock
**Address:**Main St Dublin 20
**Phone:** 353 1 2887102

#460
**The GastroPub Company**
**Category:** Gastropub, Pub
**Area:** Dún Laoghaire
**Address:**Marine Rd Dublin 4
**Phone:** 353 1 2145772

#461
**Conway's Public House**
**Category:** Pub
**Average price:** Modest
**Area:** Blackrock
**Address:**3 Main St Dublin
**Phone:** 353 1 2784934

#462
**The Ivory**
**Category:** Pub
**Area:** Dalkey
**Address:**61 Castle St Dublin 3
**Phone:** 353 1 2858327

#463
**Taste of Emilia**
**Category:** Wine Bar, Deli, Italian
**Average price:** Modest
**Area:** North Inner City
**Address:**1 Lower Liffey St Dublin 1
**Phone:** 353 1 8788188

#464
**The Audi Club**
**Category:** Bar
**Area:** East Wall
**Address:**North Wall Quay Dublin 1
**Phone:** 353 1 8663488

#465
**The Grand Social**
**Category:** Irish, Music Venues, Pub
**Average price:** Modest
**Area:** North Inner City
**Address:**35 Lower Liffey St Dublin 1
**Phone:** 353 1 8740076

#466
**Citi Night Club**
**Category:** Dance Club
**Average price:** Modest
**Area:** South Inner City
**Address:**46-49 Dame St Dublin 2
**Phone:** 353 1 6794455

#467
**Bojangles**
**Category:** Dance Club
**Area:** South Inner City
**Address:**21-25 Harcourt St Dublin 2
**Phone:** 353 1 4784066

#468
**Anseo**
**Category:** Pub, Dive Bar
**Average price:** Modest
**Area:** Harcourt
**Address:**18 Camden St Lower Dublin 2
**Phone:** 353 1 4751321

#469
**Becky Morgans**
**Category:** Pub, Lounge
**Area:** Grand Canal Dock
**Address:**9-11 Lower Grand Canal St
Dublin 2
**Phone:** 353 1 6624163

#470
**Concorde**
**Category:** Pub
**Average price:** Inexpensive
**Area:** Donaghmede
**Address:**Edenmore Avenue Dublin 5
**Phone:** 353 1 8478638

#471
**Kings Inn**
**Category:** Pub
**Area:** Bolton St
**Address:**42 Bolton St Dublin 1
**Phone:** 353 1 8725909

#472
**Out on the Liffey**
**Category:** Pub
**Area:** Thomas St
**Address:**27 Upper Ormond Quay Dublin 7
**Phone:** 353 1 8722480

#473
**Widow Scallan's**
**Category:** Pub
**Area:** Grand Canal Dock
**Address:**130 Pearse St Dublin 2
**Phone:** 353 1 6799209

#474
**Bar Code**
**Category:** Dance Club
**Average price:** Inexpensive
**Area:** Phone number
**Address:**Clontarf Rd Dublin 3
**Phone:** 353 1 8057850

#475
**La Vie**
**Category:** Bar, Polish
**Area:** Phone number
**Address:**1-5 Exchequer St Dublin 2
**Phone:** 353 1 7645177

#476
**Disco Bus**
**Category:** Childrens Parties
**Area:** Phone number
**Address:**Dublin
**Phone:** 353 85 8129226

#477
**Pure Nightclub**
**Category:** Dance Club
**Area:** Phone number
**Address:**Upper Leeson St Dublin 2
**Phone:** 353 1 2694848

#478
**Bá Mizu**
**Category:** Pub
**Area:** Phone number
**Address:**Baily Hotel Dublin 6
**Phone:** 353 1 8322691

#479
**Mullingar House**
**Category:** Pub
**Area:** Chapelizod
**Address:**Mullingar Terrace Dublin 20
**Phone:** 353 1 6208692

#480
**Fitzsimons Hotel**
**Category:** Hotel, Bar, Dance Club
**Average price:** Exclusive
**Area:** Temple Bar
**Address:**21-22 Wellington Quay Dublin 2
**Phone:** 353 1 6779315

#481
**The Glen Of Aherlow Pub**
**Category:** Lounge
**Area:** Kilmainham
**Address:**29 Emmet Rd Dublin
**Phone:** 353 1 453203

#482
**Cassidy's**
**Category:** Pub, Pizza
**Average price:** Modest
**Area:** South Inner City
**Address:**27 Westmoreland St Dublin 2
**Phone:** 353 85 8016804

#483
**Dec Gallagher's**
**Category:** Pub
**Average price:** Inexpensive
**Area:** Inns Quay
**Address:**15 Upper Dominic St Dublin 7
**Phone:** 353 1 8304572

#484
**Ryans Pub**
**Category:** Pub
**Area:** James' St
**Address:**117 James St Dublin 8
**Phone:** 353 1 6790526

#485
**Peggy Kelly's**
**Category:** Pub
**Average price:** Exclusive
**Area:** Rathmines
**Address:**161 Harolds Cross Rd Dublin 6
**Phone:** 353 1 4978935

#486
**Vicar St.**
**Category:** Performing Arts,
Music Venues
**Average price:** Modest
**Area:** The Liberties
**Address:**59 Thomas St Dublin
**Phone:** 353 1 7755800

#487
**Blue Lion**
**Category:** Pub
**Area:** Rotunda
**Address:**103 Parnell St Dublin 1
**Phone:** 353 1 8746129

#488
**Restaurant Royale**
**Category:** Dive Bar
**Area:** South Inner City
**Address:**15 Upper Stephens St Dublin 2
**Phone:** 353 1 4783097

#489
**J McGettigan**
**Category:** Pub
**Area:** Smithfield
**Address:**78 Queen St Dublin 7
**Phone:** 353 1 8721905

#490
**Ruby Finnegans**
**Category:** Pub
**Area:** IFSC
**Address:**1 First Avenue Dublin 10
**Phone:** 353 1 6264053

#491
**Liz Delaneys**
**Category:** Dance Club
**Average price:** Expensive
**Area:** Phone number
**Address:**Oscar Traynor Rd Dublin 13
**Phone:** 353 1 8474282

#492
**Donaghmede Inn**
**Category:** Pub
**Area:** Rathfarnham
**Address:**Grange Rd Dublin 13
**Phone:** 353 1 8474555

#493
**The Black Forge Inn**
**Category:** Pub
**Area:** Walkinstown
**Address:**163 Drimnagh Rd Dublin 12
**Phone:** 353 1 4557860

#494
**Graingers**
**Category:** Pub
**Area:** Baldoyle
**Address:**Baldoyle House Dublin 13
**Phone:** 353 1 8322323

#495
**Walsh's**
**Category:** Pub
**Average price:** Modest
**Area:** Stoneybatter
**Address:**6 Stoneybatter Dublin 7
**Phone:** 353 1 6708647

#496
**Palmers**
**The Golden Ball Tavern**
**Category:** Pool Hall, Indian, Karaoke
**Area:** Phone number
**Address:**Kilternan Dublin 18
**Phone:** 353 1 2955643

#497
**Grumpys**
**Category:** Pub
**Area:** Tallaght
**Address:**Belgard Rd Dublin 24
**Phone:** 353 1 4047500

#498
**Not The Eyes**
**Category:** Comedy Club
**Average price:** Inexpensive
**Area:** South Inner City
**Address:**4 Dame Lane Dublin 2
**Phone:** 353 87 9450625

#499
**Improv Asylum**
**Category:** Comedy Club
**Average price:** Inexpensive
**Area:** The Liberties
**Address:**135-138 Francis St Dublin 8
**Phone:** 353 1 4544472

#500
**Marble Arch**
**Category:** Pub
**Area:** Crumlin, Drimnagh
**Address:**1 Benbulbin Rd Dublin 12
**Phone:** 353 1 4556493

Made in the USA
Monee, IL
27 June 2021

72412544R00085